CW00657762

Dark Places

Shaun Allan

Shaun Allan

Dark Places

By Shaun Allan

Copyright © 2012 Shaun Allan

All rights reserved. Except as permitted under the U.S. Copyright Act of 1976, no part of this publication may be reproduced, distributed or transmitted in any form or by any means, or stored in a database or retrieval system without the prior written permission of the author or publisher.

This is a work of fiction. Names, characters, places and incidents are products of the author's imagination or are used fictitiously and are not to be construed as real. Any resemblance to actual events, locales, organizations, or persons, living or deceased, is entirely coincidental.

ISBN-13: 978-1-910484-03-6

Published by Singularity Books

Credits:

Editor: Connie Jasperson - Cover: Lisa Daly

* * * *

Dedication

For all the writers that need to write and all the stories that need to be written.

* * * *

Also by Shaun Allan

Sin

Hollow

MirrorMirror

Pieces of Me

Darker Places

Dorthy

And the Meek Shall Walk

A Child Called Wendy

HERO

Cell

* * * *

Visit Shaun Allan at

www.shaunallan.co.uk

* * * *

Praise for Dark Places

"Will keep you guessing"

"He paints a surreal scene that sucks you into the terror."

"Wow, a brilliantly written story!"

Shaun Allan

Acknowledgments

Sitting at a PC, the Muse strikes me. Not with a fist, but with an idea - though it takes as much force and leaves me reeling. A strange creature, part court jester, part shadow, it insists on playing with my thoughts, taking them by the hand and leading them astray. Into the darkness. Into the night.

Along the way it dances on the souls of those it passes, and it is these that I find that I must mention for it is these that the Muse steals a piece of - a hair, a smile, a frown or simply a look - to create the stories herein. I mention them to give back that which has been stolen. That which the Muse has played with and twisted into a tale darker than the smile that plays on its wicked lips.

Connie, editor extraordinaire and she who has compared my writing to that of James Joyce. Honour indeed. I thank you for your comments and your suggestions. The Muse took a strand of your hair and used it to create a web to hold this book in place.

Zoe, whose 'dark place' inspired the title piece for this collection. The Muse stole a part of your shadow and fashioned a story and an ambience. I hope that taking some of your darkness left some light in its place.

Fraser, of the dead. Your descriptions of mortuaries and the innards of... well, innards, was invaluable. The Muse opened you while you slept, just to check the colour of your own heart. I wonder if it left a scar.

Debbie, for telling me about the dragons. The Muse took a second of your childhood and used it to create a world of paranoia. That's OK. You've plenty left.

Jack, for being such a fan of Sin, you deserved your name to be in this anthology. The Muse wandered along the halls of your mind for an age, but then couldn't find its way out until Eternity's End. It was a bit peckish by then. Luckily it likes bacon butties.

My thanks are with you.

Contents

Mmmm 7

I Am Death 10

So 15

Reflections...17

This Night...19

Dark Places..21

The Coming of the Storm 36

The Last Dance...38

The Beast Within..42

Outside..44

Darkness 46

The Feast..48

Candle 50

Patient Solitude..54

Host...62

The House on the Moor...64

Feel..93

The Silence 95

You 99

The Glass..101

Look For Me 106

There Be Dragons..108

Time 116

Fair of Face, Black of Heart 118

Untitled 128

Joy 130

Shaun Allan

"Furor est in tenebris utriusque.
Debemus facere proelium cum nostra daemones."

"There is darkness and madness in each of us.
We must do battle with our own demons."

Shaun Allan

Shaun Allan

Mmmm

I look out of my window
At the darkness outside,
But it's the darkness within
That makes me feel I should die.
And the rain 'gainst my window
Cascading down,
Is the tears that I feel
When I feel I could drown.

I sit watching the T.V.
But don't see what I see,
I just surf through the programmes
Not wanting to be.
And when I'm eating my dinner,
The food has no taste,
It just ends up in the bin

Going to waste.

Going to waste, I feel I should die.
Not wanting to be, just thinking 'Why?'

Some people take their chances.
Some of us 'Seize the Day'.
Others just take what life throws,
And watch as it just fades away,
As their life goes astray,
As their dreams fly away.

I know which of these I am,
Whether I like it or not.

If it happens, it happens to me,
So I guess I'll just take what I've got.

But I wish that this was not so.
I wish I could DO,
Not just go with the flow.

But I don't.

But I can't

So I look out of my window,
At the darkness outside,
And I sigh.

Shaun Allan

I Am Death

I think that...

I think that I am Death.

I am the Grim Reaper. My cloak is in for dry cleaning (some of those stains are *murder* to get out) and my scythe is in the shop being sharpened. Still, though, I am Death.

I wander the world, plucking souls from the living like feathers from a chicken. Not that I've ever plucked a chicken, nor would I consider doing so. When I eat said deceased poultry, it no longer looks like it did when it was running around laying eggs. Well. I would assume they didn't drop eggs as they ran around, but you get my point. I can feel the pull as the soul desperately tries to keep hold of the body that has been its vessel throughout its life.

Would it be so endeared if the body was instead, perhaps, a kettle, or a bean can, or a Salt and Vinegar crisp packet? I doubt it. Something about a body, though, makes people want to stay wrapped up in the flesh. To feel the heart within beating. To know there's blood pulsing through the veins. And when they trip or they cut themselves shaving or they fight, and blood is spilled, at least they know they're alive.

Until I come along, of course. Until I make them the equal of a certain finger licking chicken.

Until I suck out their soul like the Saturday night Lottery Double Rollover Jackpot. Except, there's no six numbers. There's no bonus ball. There's no car, cruise or cottage by a lake.

There's simply me. Death. Screw that ticket up and toss it in the bin. It doesn't matter what numbers you had. You're not going to win.

Hey, that rhymed. I'm a poet. Who knew. Maybe I should bring out a book. Odes of the Reaper. A best seller in all the dungeons and dark back alleys and places no-one dares to go.

The Consequence of Life

To live is to die
To smile is to cry
To hope is to fear

To speak is to hear
To laugh is to taste
The bitterest waste
To lose is to win
To do good is to sin
To cheer is to sigh
To know is to ask why
To live is to die

Maybe I should stick to my day job, eh? Leave the poetry to those that have a heart and have a... well... a soul. A heart that still beats and a soul which still feels that beat. I'd have a hell of a time finding a publisher anyway. Most people can't see me until it's too late. Not the best idea, is it, to talk to a publisher or agent in the moments before I take their soul and watch their beloved body crumple?

I think I'll leave it. I hardly have the opportunity anyway. Being Death is a busy job. It takes up almost all my time. People need to die at all hours of the day and night. If it wasn't for Sky+, I'd never catch an episode of Coronation Street or Doctor Who.

Really, you'd think that dying could be timed better. A sign on the door of my non-existent door:

Business Hours

Mon - Thur
08:30 - 16:30
Fri
08:30 - 19:00

That'd give me my evenings and weekends free and, hey, I don't mind a bit of overtime on a Friday. Dedication and all that. But no. It's Flexi-time in the worst way. Midnight to midnight if I'm lucky. There's an interminable period of time between the end of one day and the beginning of another - at true Mid Night - when forever fits neatly into a heartbeat. The Null. Any stragglers, those I didn't get around to in the meagre twenty four hours that I had in the previous day, I have to bag then. It's like my buffer. I often wear myself out in that Null. I dash about like a headless chicken, unplucked. I can't let the Null go on for too long because...

Well... the last time that happened...

Anywho.

I *think* that I am Death.

Why do I think it? Why do I not know? I feel the pain of the dead as I take their souls. I see the instant that their skin pales a fraction as the blush of pumping blood ceases. But...

Does this make me a devil? Does this mean I'm a demon? I don't feel that I am. I do not feel either devilish or demonic. I just feel... normal. I do the things I do because I must. I turn Living into Lived because it is the way of things. I could, I suppose, be asking if you wanted fries. I could be telling you the groceries I have just scanned and bagged for you will be £87.36. More than that. They are only jobs. Means to pay your bills and so on.

I could be breathing. I could be eating. I could be sleeping. I could be doing things that must be done but take no thought. Things done because they just are.

I am Death because I *am*. You breathe because you don't know how not to.

But...

I was once a man. I was once a person. I breathed and ate and slept. I paid for groceries and said yes, I do want fries, and hold the sauce, thank you very much.

I was not always the taker of souls. I, once, had one of my very own.

Michael Connery. No, not me. The man whose bed I stand at the foot of. 34 years old. His wife of five years sleeps beside him. They've been trying for a baby for the past four years. They've been unsuccessful. It's neither's fault and they know this. Mother Nature, in her infinite wisdom, has deemed that they should not have children together. Man, in his finite wisdom, has deemed that they should ignore Nature and take things into their own hands.

Not always a good idea.

In this case, however, Man wins. She will find out in two days that the very first session of IVF they had, and the only one they can afford, has worked. She will - she is now - pregnant. She will have a boy and he will live a long life. She will not live such a long life, but it will still be more than short. A happy medium, I would say.

Michael Connery, 34 and father to a child he won't meet, will die tonight. In a moment, to be precise. He hasn't done anything wrong. There's an undetected irregularity in his heartbeat. He has, sort of, noticed it on occasion. A sharp intake of breath, a kick in his chest. Indigestion, surely. He likes his fry ups. The bacon butty. Food of the Gods.

Actually, I've never met a god who has eaten a bacon butty. Not that I've ever met a god. That I'm aware of.

I do this often. Stand before the soon-to-be-departed. I wait for a moment. Not too long, of course - I have my constraints. The Null ever waits for me to miss my quota. But I take the time to regard my intended... I hesitate to say 'victim'; it implies a vulturistic aspect. A cruelty veined with malicious intent. Such is not the case.

Michael Connery is simply the next.

Why? Why do I stand, silently looking down? Because I want to feel. I want to see if there's anything left of the soul I once had. I want to taste the acridity of remorse. I want to take the hand of the loss that Mrs. Connery will feel when she awakes at 7:30 to the beeping of her alarm. I want to embrace it and drink of it and feel it.

I know I won't. I know I can't. Such is not the way. Such just is.

I reach out and Michael's heart does its little dance in his chest, a Lambada to Life.

His soul is sucked towards me, ethereal tendrils stretching back, not willing to release its hold. Naturally, it is a pointless attempt. My hand glows by the same percentage that the pallor of Michael's husk fades.

I wait no longer. What must be done has been. I leave the room. Mrs. Connery murmurs in her sleep. I don't catch the words. The cells divide in her uterus. Did I mention it will be a boy?

Michael Junior.

Nice.

Shaun Allan

I am Death.
I know who you are.

Shaun Allan

So

The room is dark, the shadows close.
The fitful, flickering candle,
Not saving me from being morose.

Outside I hear them coming.
I'm no longer safe, no longer secure,
They'll be here soon,
With their weapons, their hate,
Smashing my windows, breaking my door.

What's left of my friends, what remains of my town,
They've tracked me to here, they've hunted me down.
So I sit in my chair, watching the flame.
Knowing it's me, I'm solely to blame.

But what else could I do? After what I have seen?
The things I have done? The places I've been?
If only they knew, if they could but see,
Maybe they'd realise that it had to be me.

But they don't, and it's done.
The game is played, no-one's won.
So I sit, and I wait,
And I welcome my fate...

Shaun Allan

Reflections

My reflection stared back at me. It looked sad. Tired. The hair was a little greyer at the temples than I remembered - my 'Mr. Fantastic' look.

I felt... empty. Like I hadn't eaten for a month. I wasn't hungry, but I did have a... hunger.

I ran my fingers through my hair, what there was of it. My reflection didn't. It simply regarded me, a sad smile shadowing my lips.

I knew how it felt.

I sighed. Mirror-me was kind enough to follow suit and we turned, looking at the floor.

My body... I didn't know it could twist like that...

Shaun Allan

This Night

This night is safe.

The air is light,

The breeze the same.

The darkness a soft, warm shroud

The sounds and the scents and the sights are calm.

This night is safe.

Up.

Up high.

The eyes tight, silver shards.

The lips tight, thin, deep red.

The features stone.

Crouching.

Waiting.

Breathing,

Barely.

This night is safe.

This night...

Shaun Allan

Dark Places

I was in a dark place.

People say that, don't they. That's not really a question, by the way, hence the absence of a question mark '?'. It's a statement. The question mark was binned in favour of a full stop, or a period if you're a menstruating American. I don't think the question mark minded being cast aside. They're lazy really, much preferring to leave all the glory to the exclamation and the hard work to the full stop (period) or comma. Only the semi-colon wishes it were used more, or at least that more people knew how to use it.

Anywho.

Dark places.

I'm not talking, really, of hidden cubby-holes, the ones where shadows puddle like liquid night, ready to pour away should the light suddenly make an illuminating appearance. I don't mean, either, the bit at the back of the sofa where your loose change teams up with that half empty cigarette packet you lost, way back when you still smoked - though there are many times when you wish you still did - to herd the balls of fluff up like dust-bunny sheep.

Oh, how you wish, sometimes, you did still smoke. You can see the tendrils of others' nicotine exhalations reaching out towards you, no matter the wind direction, enticing and teasing, willing your will to break.

No. Forget about the corner in the kitchen where the sun don't shine. Forget about the spot behind the garden shed, occupied, for all eternity, by a rusting old bicycle, the paint chipped and faded, and a mouldy roll of what was, once, fresh turf for the garden you were going to sort out before the weeds took over and you lost the Battle of Back Gardenia.

Dark places.

Of the mind.

Of the heart.

Of the soul.

But you knew that, didn't you?

Yes, a question. Edging on rhetorical, admittedly, but hey, if you want to answer, knock yourself out.

The dark places where your hopes go to die. An elephant's graveyard for the spirit. Dark enough to engulf the singularity of a black hole and still have room for dessert.

I was in a 'dark place.' Reason for suicide. Reason for self-harm.

Reason for murder.

Or excuse. You say 'tomayto', I say 'tomarto.'

You say 'potato', I say 'spud.'

It was a black and stormy night. It had to be, right? It couldn't be half past 'dentist time' (2:30) in the afternoon, with the sun streaming in through the window, dogs barking in the distance, the smell of fresh cut grass vying for your attention against the scrummy odour of freshly baked bread.

Well, it could be, I suppose. Maybe that would make it even worse. That would make it an offence against the bright, happy summer day. Horror and hate have no time for Time. They are dedicated 24/7 workers, always ready to jump in and rip your insides out.

But, in this instance, it was night and it was black. Did I mention there was a storm? Oh, good. Because there was.

The weather had been bad all week, apart from when it had been good. The sun and the clouds and the rain were all playing hopscotch with each other, chopping and changing more than a new born baby changes its nappy. Or its mother does, at least. But you'd wake up to the rain beating its way into your bedroom and, by the time your morning cuppa had cooled enough to not scorch the inside of your mouth, the sun would be making Incy-Wincy-Spider all ready and raring to climb that water-spout. Then the wind would take a deep breath and blooooow that sunshine away, replacing it, once more, with a deluge Noah would have been wary of.

The storm was one of those thunder and lightning, very, very frightening jobbies. The ones that make adults jump, children cry and dogs bark like crazy. Rain was falling so hard it was bouncing a foot high off the pavement, drops the size of marbles. It sounded as if a herd of antelope had taken a wrong turn whilst stampeding the ravine that would result in Simba's father Mufasa's death, and had, in fact, come down my cul-de-sac instead and was hammering across my conservatory roof. I suppose that would make the rest of the Lion King rather boring, and would eliminate any need for the sequels. And give James Earl Jones a bigger speaking part.

I'd long since turned the TV off. Skipping through the myriad channels of reality shows and old comedy repeats had bored me and the only program I'd fancied - a crime drama I keep meaning to follow but never get round to actually seeing - was so close to the end, the credits would be rolling before I'd even figured out what was going on. The black screen stared at me, the hazy reflections of my room looking like dusk in Alice's world. I waited for a white rabbit to run through the scene, late for such an important date, but none did. If one had, then perhaps it wouldn't have just been myself who was haunted. Maybe my own, dead spirit would have had the company of another, one that wandered my house wishing an open door would lead somewhere other than a black abyss.

Hey, I wished the same. I felt like Alec Baldwin and Geena Davis trying to leave their home but finding they were surrounded by huge, sharp toothed worms and dysfunctional family members - whichever is worse. If I stepped outside, I'd be devoured and if I stayed I'd be driven insane. There was no invading family here, just my own darkness enclosing me like a pillow over my face, but the threat was the same.

Maybe the white rabbit was really Donnie Darko's Frank, telling me the world was going to end in 28 days, 6 hours, 42 minutes and 12 seconds. At least I'd have a date, then. Something to look forward to. But Frank was off chasing disappearing cats and I was left to wonder if it was possible to step through my television screen into the matt blur of the world beyond.

And in the meantime, the rain beat at the window like the local drunk trying to get into the post office to cash his benefits so he could get his morning pint of whiskey before the previous night's bucket-full had worn off.

The remote control was still in my hand. I looked at it, momentarily confused. What was it, this oddly shaped piece of plastic? What purpose did it serve? Before my confusion had passed the baton of sense over to realisation, the telephone rang. I lifted the remote control up towards my ear; then the fact that I might be able to turn the TV on but not answer a call on it caused me to pause. I put it down and reached for my phone, somewhat embarrassed even in solitude.

Smartphones are the boon and bane of modern life. They can keep whole libraries of books, photos and music on them, keep you in Social Networking touch with a world of complete strangers and - apparently - they can even send texts and make calls. Genius. But that is their desire and their detriment. They've become more than mere aids to the modern life, a smartphone has become an extension of the person. Glued, almost symbiotically, to one's hand like an extra finger, but one too big to pick the nose or scoop the last dribble of ice cream from the bottom of the tub. Lose your phone and your life could well be at an end, and much faster than furry Frank might predict.

Mine, as was the wont with so many others, was sitting by my side, ready to leap into action at my merest whim should the occasion demand. Facebook and Twitter would declare my most mundane moments to the world in a silent tap of virtual keys and every so often an icon would pop up to say 'Hey there, you've got an email! Come on read it! Answer it! Come on! COME ON!'

They could be so demanding, you know. Always insisting you pick them up and play, whether you liked it or not, sucking the hours from your life like the battery from theirs.

I could practically feel the excitement from mine. It was like a dog that'd waited patiently all day for its owner to come home and had just heard the garden gate go.

Swipe. Press.

"Hello?"

Silence.

"Hello?"

Silence.

Whenever I normally received calls of this nature, it was from call centres wanting me to change my power to a much cheaper tariff or to tell me how much money I could claim back in PPI charges that I'd been so falsely sold, bless me. Some people hung up straight away. I preferred to (they're paying for the call, after all) wait until they came on the line so I can tell them a flat 'No' and then hang up.

You could tell, though – in those circumstances – that the other end was making a connection, that someone would be bugging you very soon. This time, I couldn't. There was no breathing, but the line didn't sound (or feel) dead.

"Hello…?"

I thought I caught a whisper. Or a whisper of a whisper. Just the edge of breath as it curved around words too faint for my ears, pressed tightly to my pocket computer, to hear. If I had, in fact, caught the whisper, I fumbled it, dropping it to shatter on the floor, the pieces skittering away like a thousand tiny spiders.

I lowered the phone and looked at it. Unknown Number, it said helpfully. Yeah, thanks.

Once more unto the ear dear phone.

Still the same undead silence.

I ended the call. A shiver ran up my back and down my arms – possibly the remnants of the whisper I probably hadn't heard.

My phone lay in my hand, replacing the remote control and inspiring as much interest. For once I didn't feel the need to check my emails or be networking of any kind, particularly 'Social.' The screen was black and, like the television, reflected both me and the room. This was clearer, though. Sharper. More in focus, as if the television needed to put its glasses on to sharpen its mirror. I was less inclined, however, to step beyond its boundaries. An unfocussed world seemed to match my own rather than this smaller, more real version.

But I ventured towards neither. Playing literal Snap (if my head was departed from my body) with the Queen of Hearts or having tea with Hatters who were decidedly Mad didn't appeal.

And they would offer no escape, anyway.

The call.

I guess I should have been freaked out by it. I wasn't. If someone had asked me what my favourite scary movie was, I may well have laughed. If there'd been heavy breathing, I'd have offered some Salbutamol. And if there'd been a throaty voice, sounding like it had smoked a hundred cigarettes a day for the last thirty years, then I'd have told my mother I'd call her tomorrow. A silent few minutes was worse, I think. Worse because it could have meant nothing or so much.

And that whisper. Or ghost of one.

Ghost. Good one. Just what I needed.

No, I wasn't freaked out. The shiver had travelled down my arms, bounced on the tips of my fingers and was now jangling in the base of my neck. It was giving me a headache. Fingers of pain were wrapping around my neck and pressing into my temples.

I wonder why it's called your temple. Do little neurons gather each Sunday and worship there, praying to the god 'Id' for a good harvest of alpha waves? Maybe the pain is a sacrifice? A ritual killing to appease an angry deity? Or, it's actually the deity itself, incensed that no sacrifice has taken place.

Whichever way the credo crumbled, I didn't appreciate this little display of religious fervour. I pressed my own fingers against my temples, willing the neurons to get back to work. After all, it wasn't even Sunday morning. It was Thursday night, so they had no excuse to be shirking their working. They clearly didn't recognise my sovereignty and continued their huddled harassment of my mind.

My heart was thumping in time to the beat of the neurons' drums, the subwoofering bass to their timpani. I knew that painkillers would be as much use as my mental mutterings but pushed myself up anyway. A couple of co-codamol may just have a placebo effect and dull the pain caused by the spiders' tap-dancing on my skull. Plus, the water might wake me up and refresh my senses.

After all, I'd turned my phone off a good half an hour before, with the intention of going to sleep. I always turned my phone off at night. The last thing I wanted was to be woken up at Stupid O'Clock by some friend who'd forgotten their address in their current drunken state, or a wrong number wondering if Tracey was in.

It had happened.

So. How could I have been called? My smart phone wasn't actually THAT smart. It didn't know how to turn itself on when someone rang. It stayed there, asleep, until I woke it, until I called it forth into action. And, this time, I hadn't.

So (again). Water and codeine.

I used to take tablets with no water, at least until I heard about ruptured stomach ulcers and internal bleeding, anyway.

I ran the tap to irrigate the stagnant liquid and took a glass out of the cupboard. By the time I'd returned to the tap, the water was running nice and cold. I took a mouthful before downing the pills and washing them on their way. Glass down, a deep breath, and back to the sofa.

My bed may well have been the better idea, but it offered no comfort to me. I felt as if, undressed and covered, I'd be distanced from my woes. The quilt my shield and my pillow my trusty steed across the land of dreams.

I didn't want to sleep, not really. Yes, I'd switched my phone off and the TV had followed suit. I'd intended to drift off, but in reality I'd known that wouldn't happen. The shadows were watching me, waiting for me to close my eyes. I wasn't going to give them the satisfaction.

But peace. That was what I really wanted. A little silence. A lull in the riotous world that spun around outside my house. I wanted, for a moment at least, the eye of the hurricane to be trained on me.

So (and thrice so), how could my phone, smart and clever and all-encompassing as it was, have burst into life and rung?

And there you have it. It couldn't have. I must have been departing this world on the first fairy wing to the Land of Nod. It must have been my imagination. That was why there was no voice, because there was no call. My mind must have manufactured it as it would a dreamstate drop, where you plummet to the earth, waking with a start just before you're pizza on the pathway.

Simple.

Of course, such is the way of the wishful thought; once you enter a dark place, you leave 'Simple' at the door.

I don't have such waking dreams. Once I'm gone, I'm gone. Granted, I can wake up at the slightest sound - maybe not a pin dropping, but a floorboard creaking, geese on the river opposite my home, something going 'bump' in the bowels of the night. But when I'm asleep, I am exactly that. Knocking out the Zeds; though I'm not sure what the Zeds have done to warrant me knocking them out.

And I don't normally dream. That's not to say I never do. Occasionally I'll remember fragments of journeys my subconscious has taken whilst I'm snoring away, but not often. Not even once a month, I'd say. And even then, fragments are all they are. Snippets of scenes which don't quite go together. A jigsaw puzzle with everything but the sky long lost.

So, so, quick, quick so. It wasn't a dream. It wasn't an imagined voice out of the ether - not that there was a voice.

It was real, in a surreal kind of way. My phone, dead to the world by virtue of being switched off, had rung. A voice had remained silent apart from the hint of a whisper. Like the call, that shade of speech might have been there and might have been an echo of my mind playing its tricks. But, if I was convinced of the existence of the call, surely...

But why? Why call? Why ring somebody up and then say nothing apart from... well... nothing! Not something they can understand, at any rate. What does it gain, other than putting the jizzles up their jazzle?

Or mine, in this case.

But then... My phone was switched off. There could have been no call, but there was. There should have been no whisper, but I was sure there was.

Thus, I wasn't freaked out as such - the temperature inside my body had taken a dive down to something only Kelvin had experienced. I was surprised that I could still feel my heart beating, that it hadn't become a heartsicle with the flow of blood solidified to become the stick. That wasn't 'freaked out'. That was, if I admit it (which I suppose I must), 'afraid.'

The shiver that was clinging Alien face-hugger-like to the back of my neck (which would make it, no doubt, a neck hugger and much less scary) shivered again. Well, it's what shivers do best.

I followed suit.

My phone was on the cushion next to me, its usual position. This time, though, it seemed to be taunting me. I glanced over to the remote control, wishing it actually did make calls, only to find it was joining the phone in mutual mockery. I was surrounded by deriding electronics and I needed to get out.

Forget sleep. Forget Alice's world beyond the television set. I needed to get outside. Fresh air. The rain to wash away my fears and phobias. The lightning to zap me back from Beyond and the thunder to grumble because the lightning was the flashy one and got all the glory.

I pulled on my jacket, and slipped my phone in my pocket. I didn't switch it back on - it didn't seem to be a requirement - but, if I left it behind, I'd feel like I was missing a leg. There'd be this long bungee cord threatening to yank me back. How dare I even contemplate leaving it behind?

Zippedy-doo-dah, zippedy up. I'd never owned an umbrella and the only hat I had was a cloth beanie (so not much cop against the elements), but I was looking forward to the feel of the water on my face. Bring it on. The laces on my trainers were loose and tucked in making them almost slip-ons, so I slipped them on. My hand was on the door handle when I had an urge to turn around.

You know, the old 'someone is watching me' syndrome. There was no-one lurking at the top of the stairs. I could see the murky reflection in the television screen and no little white rabbits, big black rabbits or somewhere-in-the-middle ghosts could be seen. And the shadows stayed exactly where they were.

I shuddered, but smiled to myself.

"Idiot."

That was the brave me talking to the not-so-brave me. The realist to the surrealist. I turned the handle and stepped outside.

The storm was in full effect. I doubted that neither Spielberg nor Cameron could re-create the likes of this deluge. Nature didn't have a budget when it came to blasting us with her power or basking us in her glory. And she didn't have anything to prove either. She'd scooped at the planetary Oscars, where the best film producers and directors could barely get an honorary mention.

I was drenched by the time I'd reached my garden gate. I could feel my clothes clinging to me and my feet felt heavy. The product I put on my hair each morning ran into my eyes causing me to blink and wipe it away. No need for the 'wet look' now. I'm sure I laughed. Not because anything humorous had occurred, but simply at the madness of venturing out on such a night. Madness, pure and simple. Part of me wanted to run, to find shelter from the downpour, but a larger part of me refused. Just deal with it. What point is shelter when you can't get any wetter anyway?

It didn't occur to me to turn and go back into my house. The call had happened there. The mirror world was in there, secretive and dusky. I was still in that dark place, but a flicker of light seemed to be illuminating the blackness out here. Perhaps Outside was too big to be that sort of dark. Maybe my inner demons could only suck the light and hope out of confined spaces. If that was the case, then maybe I'd never go back. I knew I would, at some point, though. I'd have to. I'd need food. My bed, once sleep became something I desired again. A change of clothes. My phone charger.

For now, however, the Darkness inside of me was beaten back by Nature's own blockbuster. I didn't feel free, but I felt... lighter. As if I'd been carrying someone on my shoulders and had finally put them down. Walk yourself; it's doing my back in.

Woah, now I feel floaty-light.

Indeed. Not like that at all. Just less under stress. Less cornered. Less like I could be lunch for a prowling lion at any second. Or worse. Much, much worse.

I mentioned self harm. I wish it were as simple as that.

I wish I could go back through the door of my dark place and slip right back into 'Simple' like it was a favourite slobbing jumper. The one I wore when I was having a chill day.

The one with the paint drips on and the coffee stains that won't come out. The one faded with wear and wash that I'll never throw away.

But I can't. Simple peeks through the letterbox and sniggers at me.

Self harm. It started off like that. Not in a cutting way. Not in a 'cause the pain to release the pain' way. No. Self harm in a 'now you're on a slippery slope and there's nothing you can do' kind of way. Not that I can really say what it was, but I stopped it and that started it.

Makes perfect sense, no?

No.

How you explain something you can't? How do you word something that has no words?

The rain. It was supposed to wash all of this away. It was meant to cleanse me. To, in a way, baptise me and lift me above all of THIS. But it didn't. It made me wet. It soaked me. And then it kicked back, along with Simple, and laughed full in my face. The thunder rumbled an answering grumble and the lightning flashed a dance, leaping from the clouds above to the earth below in a single bound. Superman, THAT'S how it's done!

Well.

Hey, it's not 'so' is it?

The eyes that were not following me as I left the house were also not following me out here. There was no tickle at the back of my neck - not now the shiver had dissipated at least. I didn't sense, with that pseudo-psychic ability everyone believes they have (or would like to) I was being watched.

I didn't need to. Of course there were no eyes. Of course the eyes that weren't there were also not watching me. It didn't have eyes. It didn't have anything, really. It was shapeless and shifting and shadowy.

I'd tried not to think about what exactly it was. Thing is, when you try to NOT think about something, it's exactly when you do. Right now, right this moment, don't picture a pink elephant in a tutu. If it has an umbrella held in its trunk, can I borrow it? Oh, that's right, you didn't think of it. Whatever this was, I doubted it was inclined to pirouette. Or dress in fluffy skirts.

It slid. Or slithered. No, not a slither... A sort of glide. None of these. It was like a magician's cloth being pulled away to reveal the hand beneath was no longer empty but, instead, held a dove. Except this dove would be hanging limp. Lifeless. Flesh peeling away. Feathers dropping to the floor, decaying before they touched ground.

The lightness I was feeling had been extinguished without me realising. The night folded about me. It should have been warm and welcoming, even in the storm. I enjoyed the brash exclamations of the weather when it was throwing this sort of party. I would often step outside to feel the throb of the air as the thunder and lightning battled for supremacy of the air in a modern-day dogfight. Not tonight, however. The night was claustrophobic.

Perhaps that was what this thing was. It was the night itself. Not a creature, or a shadow, or a demon of some sort. It was the night.

I saw what I shouldn't have seen. What shouldn't have been, in fact. A couple of days ago. A walk at twilight. A visit to a 24 hour shop for a loaf of bread. Pack-up for work the next day. It was warm. A little humid. Not coat and stagger weather such as this. I wasn't wearing a jacket. My keys were in my pocket and my phone was in my hand. I'd just taken a photo of the sunset - bright oranges and reds breathing fire across the darkening sky.

Along the route to the shop were little bungalows, each kitted out for the disabled or the elderly. Wheelchair ramps and the like. They were semi-detached, sitting in pairs like lovers on a swing. Between them were alleys which led to their back gardens and some fields that were mainly used by Sunday morning dog walkers and Saturday night drug addicts, the long grasses shielding them from prying eyes. The alleys were dark, but just alleys. Nothing threatening. Nothing waiting to pounce out at you.

I had heard a muffled sound as I was nearing one. It didn't register at first, not properly. A cat, perhaps. A fox. I heard the sound again and realised it wasn't an animal, but a person. Still, none of my business. An addict who couldn't wait until he'd reached the long grass. A couple of teenagers making use of a dark corner because their parents wouldn't let them alone together in their rooms.

Good for them, I thought.

But then a cry. Pain.

I was just about to press the onscreen button to cancel the camera, but stopped. In lieu of a torch, the camera flash would suit. I raised my phone and pressed the shutter.

My phone is pretty good. The camera on it too. It takes photographs almost instantly. The flash does just that, it flashes. But this time the flash didn't seem to want to go off. Or that couple of illuminated seconds dragged on in my head much longer than it did in reality, the scene before me scorched onto my eyes.

A girl, struggling. A... darkness over her, holding her down, somehow, moving up towards her face. Wanting to smother her? Though it had no features, I saw it lift up and turn to me. Then it was gone. The flash went out and my eyes were blind.

I blinked, twice, and ran to the girl, helping her up. She snatched her hands away and pushed me, sobbing, then she turned and ran.

Gratitude, huh?

If I was in a horror film, I swear I wouldn't go down into the cellar. I wouldn't. I may be dense, sometimes, but I'm not stupid. But I followed the thing, the blanket of black. Back towards the fields.

The open area was lighter than the alley, the stars and moon offering a pale luminance that was held at bay by the bungalows on either side of the alley. It meant I could see it, though I couldn't say what it was. It lay there. Waiting.

I guessed for me, so turned to follow the example of the girl, but then I saw it move. Black mercury, it expanded away from me, reaching into the grass which I could see shuddering at its touch. Then it faded. That was it. It faded. Like night becoming dawn. I expected it to slip away - or turn and attack me as it did the girl - but it didn't. It was, then it was not.

I stood for a long moment, waiting to see if I could see any more movement, but I couldn't. Shaking my head (to match the shaking the rest of my body was doing) I went back to the road and continued home.

That night I didn't sleep. How could I? When your mind can't explain something, it'll still do its very best to do so. A man levitates. It's hidden wires, of course. Or mirrors. It won't be plain old levitation. Someone narrowly escapes death. A guardian angel watches over them. Or God. Or gods. Or a little leprechaun on their left shoulder.

But this. I would assume that, if one saw a demon, one would feel the malevolence of such a creature. Its evil would ooze out of its pores like B.O. that even the Lynx effect couldn't combat. The hate would be a heat that would scorch your breath, if you dared breathe. With this there was nothing. The fear I felt was my own - spawned from an encounter with something that shouldn't have been.

The thing didn't seep sorrow. It didn't instil a feeling of horror in my heart, threatening to wrap a fist of terror around that most vital of organs and squeeze tight. It was just... wrong. It dared to defy my sense of logic, something I never often professed to possess. It attacked the girl, but I didn't feel panic or dread at that. It could, I suppose, have been a thug after her purse, or something more.

But not even that. Somehow I felt nothing - and that was what scared me. An absence of... sense. That terrified me. As if the thing numbed the 'me' inside. My soul, my Id, my dark half.

Thing. I keep referring to it as a thing. That's because of a lack of anything more descriptive. But, I know. I know what it is.

It's the night.

When the sun descends and the world goes to sleep, what does it count, instead of sheep?

It counts the lives taken. It counts the deaths, and the screams and the sorrow.

I'm walking in the rain. The raindrops hit my face in time to the rapid beat of my heart. They're almost dancing, a duet worthy of the Strictly judging panel.

Extend those arms. Straighten the back. Smile.

Without taking notice of my route, I find my feet have brought me back here. Back to the dark little alley between the bungalows. The path to the fields behind.

You need to watch your feet. You never know where you'll end up if you leave them to their own devices. But, I'm here now. I could turn and run, but I won't. I know I won't.

I have to look. I'm drawn in. Even when I see where my feet are going, I still let them take me.

And... I know what I'll see.

It's only a few steps. A dozen at most. Then I'm there. The edge of the field. It may as well be the edge of an abyss. The plummet to Purgatory.

The grass is standing straight in defiance to the onslaught of the rain. Just at the border, where the path becomes verge becomes field, I can see a trainer. White with a blue sole. A leg is attached or, rather, the shoe is attached to a foot at the end of a leg. The remainder of the body is amongst the long grass so I push forward.

You have to look, don't you. Morbid curiosity.

I reach the head. The torso is bent grotesquely, arms at angles never made during life, but legs strangely straight, a rigidity that seems unnatural considering the attitude of the rest of the body. The eyes are bulging. They are all white, as if the night has bled the colour from them. The hair is grey. It always was, at least at the temples, but now it is all a muted silver. Still, it practically shines in contrast to the pallor of the skin. The small mark on the cheek where the mole was removed is a dark line, wanting to be a mean scar but not quite managing it even in death.

I mentioned murder. Of course I mean my own. The night took me, though I wasn't a willing passenger. And there's no duty free in the Afterlife.

I think that, along with my feelings and my life, the night stole my sorrow. I look down at myself and I don't feel sad. I just don't feel. My corpse stares up at the night sky, the rain beating against the eye balls, trying to get in. I, in turn, stare at my corpse.

I turn and walk back towards my home. There's nothing for me here.

Maybe I will try Alice's world.

Shaun Allan

The Coming of the Storm

There is thunder in the distance.

Can you feel it?

Riding on

Rolling on

A thousand screams.

Can you hear it?

Blood dark, thick and rich.

Can you taste it?

Crushing on

Cascading on

A thousand dead.

A thousand dead.

Can you smell it?

Black and cold and close and tight.

Can you see it?

There is thunder in the distance.

A storm is coming.

There is no shelter to be found.

The Last Dance

The couple sat on the park bench, huddled together. They were old and the years wrinkled their skin like the bark of an ancient tree. If one were so inclined as to cut them in half, perhaps those same years would have made rings through their bodies to mark the passing of the ages.

Her hair, usually set just so, with a whole can of hairspray lending its hand to keep it in place, was wild. It was a bird's nest of wire, pulled this way and that by the wind tugging and yanking in protest, it seemed, at the lack of hair on her companion's head. If it couldn't have its fun with him, then it would double its efforts with her.

They were oblivious. He had a tear slipping down his cheek, sneaking along so as not to be noticed. She had a smile. Or the beginnings of one. Or her mouth was toying with the idea of producing one. Either way, it wasn't a frown and it was more than a simple line of non-emotion.

For a very long time, neither spoke. The one tear on the man's cheek was chased by another and, when that finally dripped from his chin (to be stolen away by the ever enthusiastic breeze), a third joined in the trail to create a continuous scar of moisture down his face.

The bench had seen better days. Once it had been a shining example of varnished perfection, and the plaque commemorating the loved, departed wife of a sad and lonely man had shone in celebration of the dawning day. Now the varnish had decayed to become tarnish. The shine darkening to grime. The smooth whittling into groove as innumerable backsides and knives and spent chewing gums had visited the seat and left their mark.

To the old man, it still shone. It still held onto, somewhat desperately, its initial glory. He saw beyond the crude scratchings. He didn't notice the carved declarations of love by teenage couples that would split within days or hours of their proclamation. The faded, splintered, peeling paint was hidden from his gaze, partly by cataracts and partly by memory.

"It's been so long," he said.

His voice was a touch above a whisper. Any louder and it would have cracked open, spilling the years of buried loss at his feet. They'd be strewn across the park by the breeze, a happy puppy with a new toy, and picked apart by crows.

The woman moved in closer. There was barely a gap between them, the air and light squeezed out to enable her to hold him as close as he needed her to.

"I know."

Her tone was a mix of sadness and fate. What was, was. The years had made their mark on him as much as they had on the bench. He bore the same scars and his gloss was faded and peeling. Neither of them could change that. Only one name beloved's name had been carved into him, however.

"But it's time."

"Past time," he said.

He was right.

Why had he survived? Why had he lingered on, when he was little more than a shade? He'd stopped living so many years ago and everything since had been... well, it had been a waste. The breaths he'd taken could have been someone else's. The food he'd eaten, what little there had been, could have fed other mouths. The beats of his heart were redundant, as his heart had been a hollow stone since... that day.

His hand reached back and touched the plaque. Tender. Loving.

He shook his head. Why did he hurt so much? Why couldn't he have just let go?

He spoke the question aloud.

"You have," said the woman.

She sat up and took his hand, pulling him to his feet.

"Why do you think I'm here?"

The old man shook his head again.

"I didn't think of that."

"Come on," she said, "Let's go."

They walked along the path towards the old bandstand where they used to dance on a Sunday afternoon, so many years before. Back when people *did* dance. Back when they felt the music in their bones and their spirit. Back when she was alive.

"When we were both alive," she smiled.

Shouts and a siren made Albert turn back to the bench. A group of people huddled around it, a couple on their mobile phones. An ambulance was parked at an odd angle, its front wheels on the grass, its rear doors wide open. Welcoming. A paramedic was bent over the body of an old man, pumping the chest repeatedly and grunting with the effort.

He shook his head at his partner. Someone cried out, a howl of sorrow for someone they'd never known and, now, wouldn't ever.

The woman pulled at his hand as the sound of a band filled the air.

"Are you dancing?" he asked, finally turning away from the sight of his body.

"Are you asking?" she smiled.

Shaun Allan

The Beast Within

I stare into the fire.
I watch its fitful, flickering feast.
And I wonder, solemnly,
If I will ever be at peace.

The night about me closes in,
It's darkness a soothing shroud.
And I sense the beasts
I feel the beasts
As beyond the flames they prowl.

But it's the beasts within I fear.
Not the beasts without, drawing near.
The dread monsters that gnaw
Far in the depths of me,
That cause me to shake,
That cause me to flee.

That wrench and tear
And cut and...

And the anger and sorrow
Boundless and cold
Seep and slide
And tighten their hold.

The beasts without draw closer.
They can sense,
They can feel,
They know that soon,

Soon...

I stare into the fire.
I give myself to the flame.
And I wonder
Shall I ever know peace again?

Shaun Allan

Outside

I'm going Outside.

I'm leaving the warmth of my room, the sensuous ease of my chair. I'm going Outside. It's cold out there. Cold and damp and grey. The dust and muck of without, airborne assailants stabbing at my eyes, raking at my nose, infiltrating my mouth to clog my innards - to take me as their own - steal about in desperate anticipation. If I turn my face to the window, I can feel the winter air reaching out to me through the glass, clawing at my cheek.

I reach over to the mighty one - the Radiator. I turn it up full. Within seconds the battle is over, the Radiator, as I knew it would be, victorious - the cold banished to its netherworld of... *Outside.*

But I'm going out there.

I can almost hear, carried on the unseen, fury-driven ghost of the wind, its cries; its Siren inspired lamentations luring me to my demise. And though I wish it were not so, though I yearn for another path, my doom is laid forth. I cover my ears to the call of the wind, but to no avail - it penetrates my defences, a haunting echo stripping me of the last shades of my sanity.

No.

It will not end thus.

My resolve hardens. No thoughts should I have for the safety of my physical being, for my soul is absolute. I will prevail.

I don my armour, in the futile knowledge of its inadequacies - my jacket offers little protection against the fearsome ruin I must face, my gauntlets less still. But I am unheeding.

I gather my wits, such as they are, and stand at the threshold of beyond. I do not look back as I cast myself over the brink of Chaos.

Hell of a time to run out of tea bags.

Shaun Allan

Darkness

The fangs drew close

The fangs pulled near

My neck, my throat

The collar clear

A pinch, a kind

Of sweetest pain

My blood to flow

Like scarlet rain

My pulse a beat

Of the vampire's drum

And then the silence

The Darkness come

And as the Reaper

Reaches in

My soul is torn

And turned to sin

I now unlive

A life immortal

Forever denied

Heaven's portal

And as the Darkness

Calls to me

I hence run wild

And let the blood run free

Shaun Allan

The Feast

Evening fell. No fanfare heralded the waning of the day. Light passed almost unnoticed into darkness, blurring through the no-time of dusk.

A newspaper, whirlpooled by a brief gust of wind, a chance encounter that created a dance of poetic uncertainty, lifted from the street to settle, spent, in a puddle by the gutter.

The air was heavy with the threat of rain. The clouds bore down, an imposing cloak that kept the stars and the moon from illuminating the world. Said world seemed... abandoned. It was lost to the grace of life and love and hope.

The street echoed with the quick footsteps of passersby who hurried, for no reason they could think of, on their forlorn way. A couple walked apart from the rest. They were arm in arm, huddled together, lost in each other, oblivious of the world's despair.

An alleyway, little more than a gasp between two buildings – a newsagents and a pizza shop – led off a little way ahead of them. The breeze that had waltzed with the newspaper drifted into the alley. It settled over a pair of sleeping cats, tattered remnants of the proud animals they might once have been. The cats opened their eyes and stretched. They padded to the shadows at the end of the alleyway, looking out onto the street, their yellow slits keen and watchful.

The larger one, a tabby with the tip of its left ear missing, lowered its head.

"Sshhh. You see them? Can you taste their scent? Does it make you hunger, desire... want? Can you feel their hearts beating? I can hear them from here - they're slightly out of sync. An almost romantic fraction of a second difference. Oh, how this feline form's senses are honed. It was a good choice, an excellent choice. For all our innate power, this creature's instincts are sensuously barbaric.

Ah, they are moving closer. You know, they are the dominant species here? Does that not strike terror into your heart? Ha! Oh, for a worthy adversary. You notice that they walk upright, that they cover themselves with the skins of other species? Such arrogance. It hints of sense of superiority over those around them. Perhaps they are, perhaps not. Perhaps, though, we should teach them that such arrogance only makes the lesson more sweetly significant. Should we, do you think, explain to them, as we dine, how erroneous their conceptions are - how their self-appointed sovereignty over their fellow creatures, only serves to prove that they are less than worthy to rule, more suited to be ornaments and food themselves. Perhaps not. They are not deserving of such benign justice.

Mmmm. They are almost upon us. Are you prepared, my friend? Excellent. Which would you prefer? The larger one? Ha! Greed was ever a virtue for you. Very well, then, if that is your choice. There is ample time for sampling other delights. The nights here are long, and we have a world of such meats to enjoy.

Come, let us feast."

Shaun Allan

Candle

I crouch to the candle,
my hands almost touching the flame,
but its heat washes past,
avoiding my sore, cold fingers.
I bear it no grudge.
Who am I to pass judgement
on a sprit as free as the fire.
The flame is company.
The flame is a friend.
Even though it denies my necessity,
the flame is a comfort yet.
The candle burns slowly.
I watch the melting wax
running down the side,
anxious to escape
the flickering feast.
I shudder.
I can see my breath.
At least I know I'm still alive,
unfortunately.
The wind howls beneath the door,
a thousand wolves fighting to gain entrance,
fighting to reach me.
I should open it.
I should give them what they want.
Me.
But, of course I don't.

As worthless as I feel,

as strong as the impulse is,

I don't.

I still, uselessly,

sit with my hands to the flame,

and wait.

I don't see the room about me,

it disappeared long ago.

Vanished along with my will.

My world is now the flame,

and my hands held before it.

I shudder again,

and I cough.

I can taste blood,

again.

The shadows whisper,

dark, sinister notions,

but I pay them no heed.

Their insights are no darker than my own.

I feel tired.

My eyes feel heavy.

I'd close them,

but I know that, in time,

I'll open them again,

to another morning,

to a dead candle.

The desire is too strong,

and I sleep,

but I was wrong.

Shaun Allan

I don't open them again.

Shaun Allan

Patient Solitude

Red Queen onto black King.

Red seven onto black eight, turn the card over.

Black two.

Deal three cards.

Red seven.

Nothing.

Deal three cards.

Black four.

Nothing.

The old man put the cards in his right and left hands together on the table and swept up the others from their separate piles into one. He picked them up, turning those were facing the wrong way so he had a neat pile once more. He drained the last of his half bitter, replaced the empty glass on the beer mat, and began to shuffle the deck.

A large man paused beside the table, picked up the empty and replaced it with a full half pint. He picked up a few coins from the collection next to the beer mat, and walked off without a word. He knew the score by now, he'd been manager of the Oak Tree pub for long enough to know old Albert hated to be disturbed whilst playing. Effectively, of course, it meant Albert (never Al or Bert) hated to be disturbed at all, seeing as all he did during the five hours each evening he spent in here was drink half-pints of bitter, one every hour and a half or so, and play Patience.

Occasionally the manager, Paul Fisher according to the sign above the entrance, tried walking away without taking any money for the drinks. Albert was so much a part of the furniture Paul felt a little guilty taking money all the time. He was never allowed, though. Albert would take hold of his arm and guide him back to the table. Without even looking up, he would pick up the money for the half bitter and hand it to Paul. At times the manager attempted to refuse the payment, but then Albert would look up, and Paul would see the sadness in the old man's eyes, and would take the money just to get away.

Paul hated looking into Albert's eyes. There was no cruelty, no hatred, no nastiness of any kind stirring in the depths. That was not what disturbed the big man. Rather, it was the desolation. Here was a man who had spent every evening sitting at this table, quietly playing Patience, for as long as Paul had been manager, and apparently a lot longer than that. Here was a man who never had any company, and hardly ever spoke apart from a nod goodnight when he left each night. Here was a man who had never won a single hand of the game he so religiously played. Not one. There was an emptiness inside this old man which Paul could feel whenever he looked into those eyes. He soon learned to just keep the drinks coming, and to keep taking the money.

Albert smiled briefly at the faded photograph of his wife which was set next to his beer mat. This was something he did before each game, as if for luck. The fact he had never won even after all these years of playing, and waiting, didn't bother him - he barely noticed.

His hands shook ever so slightly as he began dealing once again. That and the tight, grey skin shrink-wrapped to the knuckles and fingers, were the only signs that these were an old man's hands. The movements were fluid and smooth, if a little shaky. The cards were dealt evenly across the polished table-top. This was about the only table in the pub which did not have someone professing their undying love, or hatred, for someone else; Paul kept it that way, but didn't have to try too hard, no-one else had sat at this table for years. Seven neat piles of face down cards, with the topmost face up, were laid out in unhurried strokes. Once this was done, and a cursory glance showed there were no immediate openings, Albert pushed three cards from his left hand over into his right, and began to play.

Again.

* * *

The rain lashed down, a torrent almost completely obscuring the road ahead. Chris Johnson cursed out loud, adding to an almost endless stream of obscenities aimed at both the weather and every other road user in this arse-end-of-nowhere-dead-end-compost-heap. He had hated growing up here years ago, and, now that he was all grown up, and decidedly too good for this dump of a town, he could see why. God, in all his infinite wisdom, only knew why a salesman of Chris's stature had agreed to come to this backwater.

He went to flick his windscreen wiper control up another notch, and swore again when he found it was already going full tilt, and may as well have not been going at all, what with the damned river pouring down his windscreen. Chris alternately squinted and opened his eyes wide in a vain effort to see past the torrent. He knew it was no use. God, what a night to be stuck in this weather, in this town, in this clapped-out-bone-shaking-joke some malicious idiot had thought would be a good laugh to assign to Mr. Johnson. The car, of course, was none of those things. It was a brand new BMW 850, complete with every bell, whistle and wotsit known to man, which was, much to his associates dislike, pretty much justified in being assigned to the regional salesperson of the year for the past four years running. Driving a car some people could buy a house for was no consolation though, not when the wiper blades may as well have been non-existent as they were tonight.

His wife would be at home, dressed just how she knew he liked, having cooked just what she knew he liked, waiting for him to arrive with his wedding anniversary present of a fortnight in Barbados. Except he wasn't going to turn up at all at this rate, and the travel agents had screwed up with the booking anyway, and instead of going to Barbados they were booked to spent a week in Benidorm, of all the flea-pits of the world! Jenyfer was really going to love him.

Well, tough. He was in just the right sort of mood to deal with her anger.

His heart jumped into his throat as a truck leapt out of the darkness, barely missing him, and giving him another excuse to stream curses at the world. He did, however, slow down a little, and decided to stop for a break at the next pub he passed.

Christ, he'd only been going for about fifteen eternal minutes, and he needed a drink already.

A half-memory surfaced briefly of a bar with a stupid name somewhere along the road he was crawling along. He smiled for the first time that night as the brightly lit sign declaring the Oak Tree drizzled into view. Chris turned slowly into the car park and pulled up as close to the doors as he could get. He was surprised at the fairly large number of cars in attendance on such a lousy night. He managed another couple of curses as he realised the closest he could get would still mean his getting drenched before hitting shelter. Sod it, he thought, and drove right up to the entrance, parking so he could almost step directly from his car into the pub. He jumped the short distance to the doors slamming his car door while he was in mid-air. It was only when he was safely inside that he poked his hand out and activated the central locking.

Chris could have sworn he had been in this place before, when he used to live around here, but the décor and even the arrangement of the bar, lounge and toilet doors rang no bells. He didn't bother dwelling on the subject, and hastened into the lounge.

Once at the bar, he shook off his coat and threw it over a stool at the bar. He didn't notice that it was dripping everywhere, and wouldn't have cared anyway. Running his fingers through his hair, he wiped his forehead free of water, and sat down himself. With a sigh he rummaged through his coat pockets for his mobile phone, working on an excuse to tell Jan. When he finally dragged it out, his shoulders slumped. He couldn't even curse anymore. The mobile was wet, and when he switched it on, a pale flicker was all that greeted him instead of the normally bright, luminous screen and buttons.

Jenyfer could wait. He had a more pressing engagement.

"'Scuse me," he called to the barman.

The barman walked slowly along the bar, casting an appraising look over Chris. Something Chris hated was appraising looks. Especially from some lard-ass in a poxy backstreet pub. If anyone should be appraising, it should be him. And he had. And he was not happy. Just let the barman open his mouth, thought Chris. I don't need this.

"Yes, sir?" asked Paul. His appraisal of Chris's mood had been pretty accurate. The man was pissed off. From the state of him, Paul was not surprised.

"Vodka, please. Make it a large one. A very large one."

While the barman was drawing the vodka, Chris worked out the price. He was in no mood for a conversation. He put the money on the bar, and nodded at it when the barman passed him his drink. Paul was well versed in the moods of customers. He took the money wordlessly and turned away.

Chris raised the glass to his lips, threw the alcohol down his throat and breathed in sharply as the warmth radiated through his tired body. He slammed the glass down on the bar, put another pile of change next to it and nodded to the barman, who took the hint and refilled the glass.

Chris disposed of this the same way he had the first. Again the glass was planted on the bar, and again it was refilled. Chris was beginning to calm down, more thanks to the drink than anything, and thought he might even start a conversation with the barman. He turned around to survey the room, not that he anticipated having much to look at.

His gaze fell on Albert. The old man was slowly and carefully gathering up his cards and dealing them out. Chris glanced at the barman, and then pushed himself away from the bar, ignoring Paul's brief shake of the head.

He walked over to the old man's table. Old grandads, sipping bitter and playing cards - badly from what Chris could see.

Typical.

He looked down at the game in hand. What was this old duffer doing? He was missing loads of chances!

"Black four on red five," Chris said, pointing.

Albert looked up slowly, and Chris immediately recognised what Paul already knew. He backed off. Returning to the bar, he swiftly downed his vodka, signalling, as he did so, for Paul to get him another.

"What's his problem?" Chris wanted to know, noticing that the old man had gone back to his card playing.

"No problem," Paul answered, taking Chris's offered money. He didn't like this bloke. A bit of money and a lot of attitude. The guy obviously did well, his arrogance being mistaken for confidence. "He's waiting for someone. He doesn't mind losing. He'll win one day. He just doesn't like to be bothered, that's all. Never has."

Chris noticed the tone in Paul's voice. And the same to you. "Only trying to help," he muttered. He threw back the vodka, banged the glass down, and stood up. The booze was having an effect on him now. He quite liked it. Fuzzy.

His bladder urged him on, so he walked, mostly straight, to the entrance. Once through, he stood swaying a moment while he figured out the door he should go through. He got it wrong and ended up back in the lounge, looking down at Albert's cards. He swore, almost to himself, and turned back through the door, catching sight, briefly, of the picture of Albert's wife. Something in the recesses of his alcohol-dulled mind called out to him, but his bladder called louder. He found the right door.

Once relieved, Chris leaned on the basin, taking deep breaths in an effort to clear his head. A couple of vodkas doesn't have this effect. It's probably the bloody 'flu, or something, 'cos of this shitty weather. He looked at his reflection in the mirror. God, what a mess. He couldn't go home to Jenyfer looking like this. Thoughts of his wife prompted another urging from the back of his mind. Some, long buried, memory was trying to surface. Something to do with that old bloke's photo...

Chris couldn't be bothered to dwell on it. Who cares, anyway. He stood up, taking a long, deep breath through his nose. He let it out slowly through his mouth. Woah. He blinked, suddenly dizzy. Whatever it was that was struggling to be heard in his head took advantage of the drop in his defences. He looked into the mirror again and, abruptly, he knew. He'd seen that woman before somewhere. Where was it...?

Oh, God.

He doubled up over the sink, and vomited as images assaulted his senses. There was another reason he never drove when drinking. He remembered now. He'd tried to forget. He had forgotten, had buried the experience deep down. It had clawed its way out now, though. It was back, and with a vengeance.

He vomited again as he saw the car he'd stolen as a young teenager; at the torrential downpour that had obscured his sight, much like tonight. He saw the lorry which had come from nowhere, causing him to swerve off the road, and remembered the woman who had not even seen him, had not even had a chance to move before...

He retched, his stomach empty as he recalled rushing to her, seeing her neck twisted at a strange angle, seeing the blood trickling from her nose and her ears and, oh, God, from her eyes.

But she was still breathing!

Maybe she'd be OK.

He gasped as he saw himself standing up, oblivious to the rain, and then running, running as if he'd the devil on his heels.

He'd forgotten it all. But now, that photograph. That woman. He'd killed that old man's wife, so many years ago. And the old man had been waiting for her all this time. He had to get out of here. He quickly splashed water on his face, and cupped his hands under the tap to swill his mouth out, spitting the water into the sink.

There was a commotion in the foyer, people running in and out of the lounge, someone pushing his car out of the way outside. He was about to yell at them when he saw the flashing blue light coming towards the doors. The ambulance stopped, and a gurney was dragged inside by a pair of rain-soaked paramedics. They pushed past him into the lounge, returning almost seconds later with Albert strapped to the gurney, an oxygen mask on his face.

His head whirled. He had to get out. He staggered into the lounge to retrieve his coat and phone. The room was empty, even the barman had gone outside. Chris could not help himself looking at the photograph of Albert's wife, but another sight stopped him in his tracks.

On the table next to the photo were four neat piles of cards, Kings uppermost. Albert had finally won a hand. His last hand.

Chris could feel his throat tightening again, and he grabbed his coat, backing out of the lounge. His eyes remained locked on the cards until the door closing in front of him snapped him back to his senses. He turned and ran out of the pub, pushing past the crowd of gathered around the ambulance and throwing himself into his car.

His hands shaking, he managed to push the key into the ignition and turn it. The engine sprang into life, and the car lurched forward as he stamped on the accelerator. He swerved out of the car park and onto the main road.

He just barely missed the truck as it leaped out of the darkness, but he hit the wall and the windscreen and the pavement with full force.

In the ambulance, Albert's wife smiled down at her husband. He smiled back, closed his eyes, and the monitor attached to his chest flatlined.

Shaun Allan

Host

It whispers through the trees
On a breeze that's fresh and light.
Flames flicker fitfully
As it passes through the night.
Dogs go strangely quiet
As it gently drifts on by,
And people turn in their sleep
In the wake of its sigh.

It weaves,
Meandering to and fro,
As if on some dark quest,
Never pausing,
'Til at last,
It finally comes to rest.

It hovers briefly above the child,
Who stirs and murmurs low,
Then, with almost a caress,
The babe's enveloped in its glow.
The child draws breath
And sucks in death,
A vague smile darkens its face.
And a distant rumble celebrates
A new host - the Human Race.

Shaun Allan

The House on the Moor

When I first heard about the house on the moor (which was a good while before I actually saw it), I had an idea. I had a mental picture of what the house looked like - a large, rambling, run down, moody building with ivy covering one side like a comfort blanket, surrounded by a rusty iron fence which was set in a low, cracked brick wall and large wrought-iron gates that creaked with non-existent movement in a non-existent wind.

There was an old, leafless tree by the side of the property that, over the decades, had assumed a suitably demonic pose; a predatory semi-crouch with clawed branches ready to grasp at any that might be foolish enough to trespass on its territory. A grey, perpetual autumn settled (or unsettled) over the house to complete its infernal disposition.

The image was clear and acute, but then worlds and people and dreams can be born, lived, and ended in a thought, or a breath. As it turned out, I could'nt have been more wrong about the house's appearance. When I finally laid eyes on the building, I was surprised at how mistaken I had been, only about the look of the place though, only the look. The air was exactly as I had imagined. The sun could have been out and I would have shivered.

Under normal circumstances, I wouldn't have gone anywhere near. It simply wasn't my job to trawl around the country investigating houses. I could do almost everything I needed from my office. A telephone and a computer were my only tools. I didn't even have a company car. All that was required was for me to trace the owners of a certain cottage in the middle of nowhere and try to persuade said owners to sell. I had done so many times before and was sure I'd do so many times again. Usually the property had an address though… Normally I had complete autonomy when it came to the final selling price – the companies I worked for had budgets with more Zeroes than I had fingers. Their projects were vast developments that simultaneously dragged big money into an area and pissed off the locals. They wanted it both ways, the residents. They would smile as estate agents valued their homes at a couple more grand than before the shopping precinct opened or the leisure complex (complete with multi-screen cinema) began to draw in crowds. Then they would scowl at the hordes of people invading their territory and at the noise and the mess and the increased traffic.

Never happy.

But that didn't concern me. I was the residents' friend. I was doing them a favour. Maybe they didn't really want to sell, but add a couple of grand on the estate agent's couple of grand and they began to agree. Add ten and they were practically naming their children after me. After all, I'd tell them, the Company never did me any favours, did it?

To be honest, that was more the truth than anything was. They didn't do me any favours, but they paid my wages.

So. They wanted to build somewhere, and a house, or a street (once or twice even an estate) happened to be in the way. How inconsiderate. But I was good at my job, and I got results. I'm a nice guy, essentially. Perhaps my job had me doing things that, if I thought about them, I might find disquieting, but I didn't think about it. I'm a nice guy, and I could, it was felt, be trusted. The Company liked that, so they used it.

This particular project was something of a new direction for them. I didn't know the details, but I rarely did. All I knew was that they needed to acquire some land on the edge of the North Yorkshire Moors and aerial photographs had revealed that someone had plonked a house right in the middle.

I had the maps. I had the reports saying there was a house there. I had a grid reference. The photos had taken a detour somewhere on their way to my office, but I was used to that kind of thing. I often wondered if I worked in the equivalent to Heathrow's luggage claim. Mail and reports meant for me would appear on desks along the corridor or on another floor. It was normal. I didn't even notice that much anymore. They'd turn up.

The first thing that struck me as odd was the lack of an address. There was a grid reference, but it wasn't the same as 31 Chatham Avenue or somesuch. It would just take a little digging that was all. A computer (and the Internet) is a wonderful thing, and with the right passwords you can find out pretty much anything you want to know short of what your next door neighbour had for breakfast (although you could hazard a guess). So I dug.

Three weeks later I'd still found nothing. The house seemed to have been on that land forever, yet nowhere could I find a record of anyone actually owning, or building it. I unearthed various references to it in texts, surveys and even in some folklore (apparently it was haunted!). Possession (perhaps an inappropriate word considering the place was meant to be inhabited by ghouls and ghosts and that sort of nonsense) may well have been passed down through innumerable generations, but there should have been somebody sitting at the top of that particular tree. There wasn't. The deeds seemed to be non-existent. They could be locked away in a safety deposit box at Barclays, or hidden in an old shoebox under a pile of faded black and white (or grey and cream) photographs for all I knew. No one was laying claim to the property and I was beginning to get annoyed, not least because the Company was getting annoyed. I only really had one option, and that was to visit the place.

The journey took four long hours. It should have been much quicker, my office wasn't that far away from the moors, but the house was set back against their edge. Not a problem, one would think. Unfortunately, the nearest road was two miles away, the nearest town was thirty miles away, there were no signposts saying 'This way to the Middle of Nowhere', and I had a crap sense of direction. The weather was bad – it admittedly wasn't Hurricane Annie, but it was a wee bit worse than Winnie the Pooh's Blustery Day! The wind was strong enough to make me wrestle more than once with the steering, and the windscreen wipers were woefully inadequate for the downpour. I had passed where I needed to leave the road three times before I stopped to get my bearings. The road was completely non-descript – a single clean track of tarmac without even a white line to break the monotony. I had been along it and back again feeling my search was more and more fruitless as I went. It occurred to me that perhaps the photos were wrong. I hadn't actually seen them myself, and had forgotten they weren't in my file. A small red dot on the map was all I had to go by. Maybe that was why I couldn't find the place. Maybe it wasn't really there and the photographs had really shown just an old fallen down ruin – a shack that had once housed a farmer and his wife, their two daughters and the obligatory dog. Perhaps it wasn't even a building – it could simply be a mass of dead trees or something similar. The Moors were not one of the most hospitable places I had visited. Still, I should at least attempt to find it, if for no other reason than to satisfy my own, somewhat idle, curiosity.

I stopped my car to take another, more concerted look at the map. The road wasn't wide enough for more than one car to drive along at a time (if two passed each other I was sure one would end up on the mud verge) so I simply stopped where I was. The tarmac didn't look as if it was exactly well travelled so I didn't see any reason to worry that another vehicle might come careening along. Besides, it was a practically straight road. Any cars wouldn't simply leap out of nowhere.

The map was one of those huge foldout affairs, the kind that never quite folded back the same way that they unravelled. I hated them, but they served their purpose. Originally I'd had a few scans of the area, but they were next to useless for finding somewhere that probably didn't even exist. I'd transferred the little red dot-marks-the-spot onto this monstrosity to be able to trace it from the nearest town. That wasn't as easy as I had first thought, though. Sure the main road was right there on the map, I'd traced it with the same red marker I'd used for the dot. The lack of any road or even rut in the mud to the house meant I had no real idea where to turn off. The terrain was too rough for my meagre Mondeo so I regrettably conceded that I was going to have to walk. This was where my major indecisiveness came in. I didn't fancy wandering around on the Moors for the rest of my days. I had seen the films – the moorland was inhabited by unwholesome beasts, eager to lunch on whichever part of your body their teeth bit first. It was either that or I'd end up with my foot getting caught in some pothole or other and be stuck fast. I had already checked my mobile phone and was unsurprised to find there was no signal. I could end up lost or dead and have no way to contact anyone either way.

OK, so I was being paranoid. I was looking out of my window and seeing nothing but nothing and I didn't fancy it. The downpour had abated, but the wind was still strong enough to bend what few trees I could see. I liked towns. They were cosy. I'm not even slightly agoraphobic, but I much preferred to be surrounded by houses and people than empty space with only a willow to keep me company. I had a dog. I took him for walks in the woods nearby. That was nice, and that was enough.

Well the quicker I did this the faster I'd be done. Or something.

I took one last look at the map; there was no way I could take it with me – if I tried to open it I'd probably have it snatched away by the wind. There were no real landmarks for me to have had any idea where I might be if I got lost, so I threw it in the back seat. I didn't bother to fold it; I didn't want to still be here tomorrow. Zipping up my woefully inadequate jacket, I stepped out of the car.

The first thing that I noticed was that it was bittingly cold. Well, actually that was the second. The first thing was that the gale had, in the absence of the map, decided to snatch my breath. It was whipped away as if the wind had reached in an invisible hand and wrenched it from my throat. It took me a moment to recover and by then I realised I was shivering. I cursed my insanity. Come back tomorrow, I told myself, the weather may be less uninviting. But then it probably wouldn't be. This was England, and England delighted in serving up great dollops of awful weather for her patriots. Besides, I was under pressure on this. I knew full well that I was not going to be getting back in my car until I'd found this house. I breathed into my hands and rubbed them together. It had no effect so I plunged them deep into my shallow pockets and set off. I knew the house was supposed to be about two miles from the road, so I figured if I walked straight out that distance, I could then turn right and walk a ways to try and find it. If that didn't work, I'd simply turn around and go the other way. If I still couldn't find it, I'd come back to the road and then try to find my car. I had a certain level of determination, but I wasn't totally averse to simply giving up.

The ground was firm, which was somewhat refreshing. It would have been just my luck, I thought, to find myself wading through mire. Granted the grass was just short of knee length, and wet (soaking my trouser bottoms in minutes), but walking was relatively easy. I was thankful for small mercies. I realised, as I went, that the most walking I did was either taking Tilly, my dog, for a walk, or going to the coffee machine at work. I had no real idea just how far two miles was, and I figured distances out here, where the only thing stopping you seeing forever was the horizon, would be hard to estimate accurately.

I was depressing myself, I knew. There was quite a lot to see if I actually bothered to look. Trees, the names of which I had never really bothered to learn, dotted the landscape. I knew what a willow and an oak looked like and that was it. Both of these resided outside the pub my parents frequented. I had spent many a Saturday afternoon waiting outside that particular hostelry (named The Oak Tree for obvious reasons) waiting for my mum to just nip in to get my dad, and only having the one drink while she waited. Once, I remembered, I had been standing under the tears of the weeping willow when there was a loud crack and the thick branch above me slowly snapped and fell on me. I have no idea why I simply stood and watched, but that's just what I did. Luckily I was standing out towards the end of the branch, which must have measure 12 inches across. I had been pulling at the leaves and the next thing I knew I was in them. I was still standing there, waist deep in tree, when my mum finally came out. She didn't believe me, but I didn't really mind. I wondered, at the time, if the 'weeping' willow had cried so much it had been broken by the weight of its tears.

I looked behind me to check my bearings against my car. I could still see it, a small white scar against the grey of the clouds. I was surprised at how far I'd managed to walk. Hell, maybe this wasn't going to be so bad after all. I turned back and continued on, scanning the countryside for any sign of a building. I could see the Moors now, rising up from the flats like a – well - like a load of hills. I realised I had lost my imagination around the same time I was accosted by the willow. The realisation made me sad – I'd never noticed it was gone, slipping away like the proverbial thief-in-the-night. Sure, I could make clichéd metaphors, but I didn't want that, not any more. I wanted to wake up the kid in me, assuming he hadn't sneaked away under the cover of my imagination. Why I was thinking like this, I couldn't fathom. I was a practical person and hadn't particularly suffered from its absence. I didn't know if it was due to the fact that, for the first time in forever, I was totally alone with my own thoughts. Perhaps it was because I wasn't used to open spaces or silence (ignoring the violent gale) and my mind had been working overtime on this blasted house. Either way, I needed to perk myself back up. I thought back to my youth and the trees I'd climbed (and fallen out of). It worked, to a certain extent. At least I could concentrate more on the job at hand instead of wallowing in inconsequentials.

After what seemed an age, and noticing I could no longer see my car, I stopped. I guessed this would be about far enough, and I should be able to see the house if I came within a good distance of it. I mentally flipped a coin to decide which way I should turn, and it came up Heads. So left it was. There was still no trace of a path of any sort and wading through wet grass, no matter how relatively short it might be, was tiring. The wind seemed to be hitting me from all directions while still being mainly right in my face, even though I'd changed my bearing. I couldn't see the road or my car, but to my right were the beginnings of the Moors.

They rose fairly sharply in a straight-ish line ahead and behind me, about a couple of hundred yards away. Mist clung to the slope giving a vague veiled look, as if they were slightly out of focus. It felt colder. I could see, further away, plateaux and hills rising to scary heights. I was so pleased my goal wasn't way up there.

As I walked, I realised the 'straight-ish' line was really nothing of the sort. The edge of the Moors dipped in and out like a coastline. Even with the roar of the gale I could sense a heavy silence from that direction, as if the storm couldn't quite touch it. This hush was emphasised by the stillness of the fog – it might have been a painting it was so calm. It was strange, I thought, the tricks your senses played in unusual circumstances.

I returned to my scrutiny of the Moor's 'coastline'. Various sized coves broke its edge creating small, and sometimes not so small, shelters from the elements. Branches and bushes had found their way into many, torn from their original abodes by the relentless wind. It was eerie and added to the desolate feeling. It seemed I had, at the most inopportune time, rediscovered my imagination. I was just walking across a blustery field. Granted I was in the middle of nowhere and alongside the North Yorkshire Moors, but it certainly wasn't anything creepy. As for the brushwood in the 'coves', it did not look like grasping hands – it was simply deadwood. The mist along the rise of the Moors was not a ghostly veil, hiding untold horrors, and the fearsome breeze was not a Banshee scream. I knew all of this. I knew all of this. My only problem was convincing myself of it.

I was getting tired of this. The house could be anywhere or nowhere. I knew I had intended walking in both directions, but I just couldn't be bothered. I'd tell my company that it was clear – the land was OK. A few grand to the local council would secure it and they could go ahead. The decision was made and I was about to return to my car when I saw the post. It was wooden and rotten and mostly moss covered, but its regular, artificial shape stopped me dead in my tracks.

A fence post.

I drew a long breath through clenched teeth and let it out through my nose. A little further along, the moor edge slipped back again. The post was lying, pointing in no particular direction, just before the gap. The house was very likely set back in this bay – a natural place to set up home, as it would provide ample refuge from storms and the like. I used the term 'natural' even though I couldn't imagine why someone would want to build here. I didn't understand why I was suddenly so anxious. All I had to do was knock on the door, speak to whoever lived there, and go home. If nobody was in residence then I'd probably have a look round, but then I'd leave. It was nothing major.

Still, apprehension wrapped its wiry arms about my chest and squeezed.

I moved forward.

I sensed rather than saw movement out of the corner of my eye and snapped my head round. I swore at myself when I saw it was simply the swirl of the mist as it rose up the hillside. Well, that ruined the image of a painting. Perhaps I should have thought it strange that only now had the mist decided to stir, but I didn't. I had continued walking while my attention was on the swirling fog and, when I turned back, I realised I was now at the gap, having stepped over the decaying fence post without noticing.

The house was before me, in all of its unnatural glory. I was, frankly, disappointed. What faced me now was a shack compared to the epic manor my newly found imagination had created in my mind. I certainly couldn't see Herman Munster answering this door! In fact, if the front door were opened, it would probably fall off its rusty old hinges! Yet still trepidation tapped me on the shoulder.

A dishevelled and scruffy looking attempt at a garden was surrounded by an equally bedraggled low wooden fence, the sort with four inch tapered posts rammed into the ground with thin wooden slats nailed against them. Most of the slats were broken and lay lazily in the long grass. Those that were still more or less in one piece seemed to hang onto the stakes precariously. The posts themselves were in much the same state of rot as the one I had carelessly stepped over. They were leaning unsteadily at all angles as if they simply couldn't be bothered, or didn't have the energy to stand upright. Some were missing, although I could only see the one at the cove entrance, giving the fence the look of some beggar's mouth – gaps in teeth that were almost lost themselves. A gate, fashioned in much the same way as the fence, allowed entrance into the grounds. It creaked quietly as I opened it. A green scum coated my fingers where they had been in contact with the gate and I hastily wiped them in my handkerchief.

The garden reminded me of my own hair when I had just woken up. The term 'dragged through a hedge backwards' came to mind. Coarse grass, the same length as the field I had just traipsed through but with a more sickly appearance, covered the area from the fence to the house. A narrow paved path ran to the front door in much the same condition as everything else – it was cracked and uneven. I paused half way along it to take a proper look at the building. House was too grand a word for this abode. Cottage would just about come close, though it was barely beyond a hovel. It had two floors, with a number of small windows, the glass of which was amazingly still intact (if dirty). The roof was thatch and had seen better centuries, let alone days. It seemed to have been rendered with a dash of pebbles sometime in the distant past and patchy remnants still stuck to the walls. The door looked about ready to collapse. It was scratched and peeled and cracked, scarred by time and the elements. I could see the rust of the hinges from where I stood. The handle was missing and I could see no evidence of a lock.

I could also see no evidence of habitation. I walked up to one of the front windows and peered inside. The window was reasonably large with no curtains or blinds to obscure my view inside. The day, though cloudy, was still fairly bright, yet despite this the interior of the room was gloomy and dark. I shielded my eyes as I looked in but it had no effect. The room was a mass of shadow, almost as if it was hiding from me. I shook my head and moved to the other side of the door. This window was slightly smaller than the first, which I thought odd – I always figured houses with a door in the centre should be made symmetrical, but I always had to put a cup down at right angles to the surface, so I couldn't really talk. Again, the contents of the room within were withheld from my view. I could vaguely make out shapes, and didn't think there was any furniture to speak of, but I really couldn't be sure.

I stepped away and walked around the side of the building. Only one small window adorned this wall, high up near the eves. Now that was where the killer would be hiding, twitching the nets. As with the other windows, there were no nets, but a shiver still raked down my spine. When I reached the back of the house I stopped. The mist from the Moors, thick and glutinous, rolled down right down to the back door, shrouding the entire rear of the building. I couldn't see the door or any windows and could hardly make out the structure itself. Mist shouldn't be like this, I thought. Mist is vaporous and insubstantial, not this viscous gloop. I didn't like it, but had a few choice words with myself to calm my nerves. It was a house! Nothing more! It was a bit of fog, nothing more! Get a GRIP!

I turned abruptly and walked, as confidently as I could, back to the front. I needed to do something positive here. I needed to get a hold of myself and do my job. The house didn't particularly look that scary. It was simply an old, haggard looking building and I needed to find out something about it. Anything.

I would have to go inside.

I looked at the front door. It was still cracked and peeling, but now it appeared to be sneering at me. "Come on," it was laughing. "Enter if you dare." Cue Vincent Price cackle. I laughed back at it. "I dare," I said out loud. The words sounded flat and completely unconvincing, but they served to bolster me just a touch. I practically marched up to the mocking door and purposefully pushed it open. It creaked, naturally. The obligatory sigh whispered past me as the musty air from within met the fresh air from outside. Amazingly, I didn't associate it with anything ghostly. I was quite proud of myself. I stepped inside and closed the door behind me (before it could mysteriously close by itself).

I was in a small hallway, with rickety stairs leading up to a short landing. It was gloomy, but at least the house seemed to have come out of hiding – I could see easily. The floor was bare, unvarnished boards and the walls were covered in a faded brown paper that was heavily water stained, the blemishes creating more of a pattern than had already existed. There was a closed door to my right, near the bottom of the stairs, which resembled the front door in condition, and another similar one at the far end of the hallway ahead of me. I knew there was a room to my left (the first one I'd peeked into), but no doorway allowed entry from here. There wasn't much of a dank smell, which I would have expected, but there was a faintly fusty odour. The whole hall, and this probably went for the rest of the house, gave the impression of being rusty, almost like the hinges of the front door. It had a corroded feel to it as if, at any time, it might simply collapse in on itself. I was reminded of the final scenes of Poltergeist, where the house imploded in a supernatural ball of light.

I stepped forward. I thought I'd try the rear of the house from the inside, figuring there'd be a kitchen back there. The first place I ever looked for anything important, even if I was sure I hadn't put it there, was the junk drawer in my kitchen. Eight times out of ten it would mysteriously find its way there. Perhaps any owner of this house had the same methods. It was somewhere to start anyway. It was clear, from the state of the hallway that no one lived here currently.

I was about halfway towards the door, my footsteps on the wood echoing lifelessly in the numb air, when I heard a loud crack. It sounded like a cross between a gunshot and something familiar that I couldn't quite place. I looked around but could see nothing. Then I looked down at the floor. A line, roughly oval and with me in the centre, had appeared in the wooden floorboards as they suddenly splintered apart. I realised why the sound had been familiar. It was exactly the same as I had heard so many years earlier standing beneath the weeping willow as the bough had broken and I'd found myself in the midst of its tears.

Before I could move to the stairway or back out to the front door, the flooring gave way beneath me and I fell into the darkness below.

I blinked.

For a moment, I didn't quite understand where I was. I should have been lying broken in the damp cellar of this rotting house, but I wasn't. I was standing on the edge of the hole. Perhaps I'd managed to jump at the last moment. Survival instincts and reflexes can be uncommonly powerful when needed and it wasn't, I supposed, beyond the realms of possibility that I had leaped out of harm's way and not realised it. I could think of no other explanation and it took a few long minutes for my heart to calm and my breathing to steady. I noticed that it had turned colder in the hallway and I could see my breath as I exhaled. I rubbed my hands together briskly even though I didn't really feel that cold. The floorboards were creaking quietly as I stood, slightly swaying, and I knew I needed to move away from the hole – I might not be so lucky if the same were to happen again. I hadn't realised I suffered from any form of vertigo, but I couldn't bring myself to look down into the opening. I didn't feel safe.

I slowly moved along the corridor toward the door at the end, keeping my back against the wall. Maybe I should have gone back out of the front door, but insanity had dragged me thus far, so I figured I'd stay along for the ride. A draught must have been coming up from the cellar because, as I neared the door, I noticed I could no longer see my exhalations. I reached the door and opened it. There was a slight rasp as the hinges protested after so many years of disuse, but I no longer had any misgivings about my exploration. I'd have thought I'd be hastily making my getaway before the rest of the building crashed down about my ears, but my narrow escape seemed to have steadied my nerves. I could have been wandering around my own home.

I'd been right in my guess. A small kitchen welcomed me after the concerns of the hallway. It was long and not very wide and had a low window next to the back door. There were no appliances, such as a cooker or refrigerator, simply a large sink and a plain wooden table with a couple of plain wooden chairs pushed neatly under. A faded picture hung limply on one wall, perhaps a flower or something similar (I could make out some sort of stem with what looked like a head but that was all – maybe petals but I couldn't be sure). The window looked, at first glance, to be whitewashed and obscured but a closer inspection showed that not to be the case. The fog that had prevented my investigating the back of the house (ok, so it was my own nerves, but I wasn't going to start splitting hairs) hugged the window. There was no gap or interruption in the mist; it seemed to touch the window over its entire surface. It still appeared as unnaturally thick as before, and moved not in the swirl I'd have expected but with more of a kind of shiver as if it was trying to keep still but was being agitated by something I couldn't see.

On the table was a rectangular wooden chopping board and a carving knife. I picked the knife up, testing its dull edge. It looked worn but as if it was blunt with time rather than use. I returned it to its place on the chopping board and looked around again.

The kitchen had three doors. One was the exit to the left of the window, which I contemplated trying next. There was the entrance to the hallway and a third on my right. I couldn't understand this. It meant the room on the left didn't actually have access into it, while the one on the right had two. I shook my head and decided to see what was so special about the right hand one that needed two ways in – or, I suddenly though, a way in and a way out… Of course a room with no doorway was even stranger, but I'd look into that later. I forgot about the window and its blanket of mist and entered the room.

It looked moderately large, but that was mostly due to the lack of furnishings. The floor was bare, lacking even the most threadbare of carpets. No pictures adorned the walls, or even wallpaper for that matter. The room was little more than a shell – empty and barren - but it had a pervading sensation of obscurity. It was like a shadow at the edge of my vision that I couldn't quite focus on. It certainly wasn't as dark as it had seemed from outside, but the impression of a lingering dusk hung on my eyes. I walked to the window and looked out. The wind had picked up again and a spattering of drizzle sprayed the glass. I could see the grass being whipped about and, uninviting as it looked, I had a sudden urge to be out there, walking back to my car and my home and my dog.

I turned back to the room. Its complete lack of décor gave it an eerie feeling, bleakness almost. I shivered and walked back to the kitchen, not wanting to chance the floor of the hallway again. As the first floor was out of bounds to me as well now, and the other room was sealed off for whatever reason, my only option appeared to be outside. The fog had not abated and still twitched curiously against the window. I might not be able to see where I was going, but I could feel my way round to the side of the house. If the land began to rise, I knew I'd have to turn around immediately and return to the house, or run a risk of ending up lost on the Moors. Echoes of The Hound Of The Baskervilles ran fleetingly through my mind and I paused with my hand on the door handle.

I shook my head and again had to laugh at myself. Apart from the near accident in the hallway, not a single thing had happened to me in this obviously deserted building. Perhaps outside was precisely where I needed to be. I pushed the handle down and pulled the door open.

A fetid stench of absolute decay assaulted me as tendrils of mist reached in like skeletal arms. I was very nearly sick and had to cover my nose and mouth with my hands to prevent me from retching. My eyes were streaming and I stared wildly as a feral growl, low and guttural, crawled out of the fog.

At first I could see nothing, then a dozen or more pairs of crimson eyes, like slashes in the mist, came rushing towards me. I fell back and kicked the door shut, then scrambled to my feet to make sure it was closed properly. I was knocked back as body after body hurled itself against the other side. I had no idea how such a dilapidated door could possibly hold such a force, but hold it did. I backed away slowly, my body shaking uncontrollably. My mind raced. What were they? I'd been walking out there for an age! I could have been attacked at any time! How could I get away from here without them coming after me? What were they???

I'd had the impression of some great lupine shape, but all that I could see in my mind were those brilliant red eyes saturating me with their stare. I was still backing away when,

suddenly, I was surrounded by sound. It was so abrupt and…
complete, I felt almost bathed in noise. Voices whispered my
name. I heard cries and growls, soft singing and raucous laughter.
It was all entwined in a constant stream that filled my head. I
looked around me. And I screamed.

My body was half way through the wall. My left leg was
already through, with my torso and head following. I staggered
back, a terrible cascade of vibrant colour blinding me.

I fell to the floor and the clamour stopped. The reek
from outside had failed to turn my stomach completely, but this
latest episode finished the job. I'd had a simple breakfast, early
this morning, of toast and black coffee. What was left of it was
now pooling on the floor in front of me. It had been one simple
clench of my stomach and the sensation was gone. I coughed
twice and pushed myself weakly to my feet. I looked at the wall,
noticing the house was once again silent. I shook my head.

It must have been an illusion of some kind.

Yeah, that was all. Trickery.

I went to the wall and, very tentatively, reached out to it.
It felt solid – slightly rough with a dusty texture. I pushed at it
and then slammed the palms of my hands against its hard surface.
It wouldn't give, yet there must be some way through! I rubbed
my hands over the entire wall, searching for some dip or hidden
catch that might indicate a concealed exit. There was none.
Becoming more frantic, I continued my search across the rest of
the room, turning my attention to the bare floor and cracked
ceiling when the walls proved fruitless.

There was nothing. The only way out seemed to be the
window. Unfortunately, it didn't open and I had nothing to throw
at it (except myself) to smash the glass. I was not quite at the
stage where I could hurl myself through a window, but I knew I
was getting close.

Besides, night was falling. I didn't realise I had been in
here that long, but it was definitely growing dark outside. In the
deepening dusk, I sat in the middle of the floor and hung my
head in my hands.

What were those creatures outside? Wolves? Did wolves have eyes like that? Was there any way possibly that I could outrun them all the way to my car?

I didn't think so.

And how did I get in this room? It looked, and felt, like I walked through the wall! How was that possible? What was all that noise? All that colour?

My head spun. I felt like a whirlpool was inside my mind sucking me down. I looked over at the window staring at my reflection. Whatever had happened when I'd entered this room must have affected my sight because I looked slightly blurred in the glass. I rubbed my eyes and looked again. I still appeared to be out of focus. I looked at the rest of the room. It was clear and well defined – almost overly so, as if the corners were sharper and the surfaces were somehow more intense.

But my reflection was indistinct. Fuzzy.

A thought tried to creep into the back of my mind, but I pushed it away without letting it form completely. It was quite ludicrous. But it wouldn't settle. It was determined to be heard. I stared at the wall in front of me, separating this room and the hallway.

What if…?

I breathed deeply, telling myself that I was being immensely foolish, but I knew I was not. I stood up slowly and looked over to the wall I'd come through originally. There was no door. I could pretend that it was an illusion if I wanted. I knew it wasn't. I could lie to myself and say I'd been tricked somehow. I knew I hadn't.

I faced forward again and closed my eyes. I drew a deep breath once more. My nose whistled off-key as I let it out. Keeping my eyes shut tight, I lifted my arms into a typical 'zombie' pose and walked forward.

I hoped I would hit the wall. I wanted my hands to make contact on the bare plaster. If they had, I could possibly have made a break for it through the window, risking cuts and a mauling by those weird wolves to run back to my car. Tomorrow I would tell the Company that they could tear down this place and build their new development. If my hands touched the something solid, I'd even offer to drive the first bulldozer.

They didn't. I tried to tell myself I just hadn't reached it yet, but then I heard my name whispered. Before I knew it I was wrapped in sound again, a cacophony of noise that was simultaneously a jumble of sound and totally distinct strands. I opened my eyes to a vivid cascade of images that seemed to deafen me more than the noise itself. I staggered forward to the bottom step of the stairs and the assault ceased abruptly. I was leaning heavily on the banister, my breath heavy, when I saw the hole in the floor. I'd forgotten about that. I supposed I should look down into it, now my fears had been confirmed. I was shaking, though not as much as I would have thought I'd be. A section of flooring was still attached to the bottom of the stairs and I stepped carefully onto it. I looked down.

My body, broken and bleeding, lay on the splintered remains of the hallway floorboards. My arms and legs were bents at odd angles, looking like a child's action figure that had been tossed casually aside. My head was facing the wrong way. I laughed coarsely, thinking I finally had eyes in the back of my head. Three stakes, wooden shards from the flooring, pierced my torso at various places. Blood had soaked my shirt and was forming a puddle around me, outlining my figure like the chalk from a police film.

I waited for the horror to strike. I waited for the realisation that I was dead to reduce me to a quivering mess. It didn't. I waited for a dazzling white light to appear, a bright tunnel, perhaps, to stretch out to infinity. Neither materialised. Instead, I felt an odd detachment. I stared down at my ruined body, and felt completely indifferent, as if it really was a casually thrown children's toy.

It was light again when I next moved. Time, it seemed, had a somewhat different meaning to those dearly departed. Daylight streamed in around the loose frame of the front door, making the hallway seem almost welcoming. Yeah, I thought. Come in, make yourself at home. You don't mind plummeting to your death do you? Good, good. Let me take your coat. Whether this was said mentally or out loud I didn't know. Not that it mattered, really. I was dead. It was pretty much the same either way.

Saying that felt weird: "I'm dead." It was like saying "I'm Shaun." I imagined meeting someone at a party or somewhere similar. "Hi, I'm a ghost," I'd say. "Oh, hello," they'd reply. "I'm a doctor."

I diverted my attention from the corpse in the cellar to the hole itself. It was large and fairly regular, almost artificially so. For a moment I wondered if it had been deliberately cut, a deadly reprisal for any trespassers, but I saw how the exposed ends of the floorboards were splintered and split. They were rotten and simply couldn't take my weight. I smiled to myself, which was bizarre under the circumstances. I realised I was the other side of the pit from the door-less room, yet I had walked (eyes closed) straight across it to the stairs. Perhaps this ghost business had its uses. Well, I thought. I may as well have a little practise.

I glanced, automatically, at my watch. I laughed, then, to see that I actually still had one. Not only that, but it still worked! The second hand was sweeping round as usual and the date had moved on to tomorrow (or rather today). I thought that was ever so slightly amazing. I looked down at my left wrist to see what state my 'real' watch was in but a bloody sleeve covered it. I checked my watch again. I wasn't aware of watches having souls (or whatever my present form might be), but there it was. I pressed the illumination button and the dial sprang into luminescent blue 'life'. I shook my head in wonder.

Having a watch, real or otherwise, on my wrist did, sort of, indicate that an idea I had might be true. To try to prove it, I stepped backward. Looking down, I noticed that I couldn't see my feet. Midway along my shins, my legs stopped and a step began. I could hear vague echoes of voices, a drastically diminished version of the onslaught from the wall. I lifted my foot and placed it on the step, pushing myself up so both feet were on the stairs. I touched my hand to the wall and felt the slightly rough contours. I could run my finger along a faint crack. Taking a deep breath, I pushed. My hand sank into the plaster to the wrist, and somewhere inside my head I heard my name whispered over and over. I could feel nothing in my hand to show it was encased in brick. Without pulling it back, I lowered my arm to my side. It slid through the wall without resistance.

Stepping onto the floor, I sat at the edge of the hole, dangling my legs in the cellar. I could feel my heart thumping at I stood again and, without pausing, walked forwards. I could feel the floor beneath my feet. I could hear my shoes scraping on wood that wasn't there – that was now impaling my battered carcass under me. I looked down and fancied I could even see the floorboards in their original state but insubstantial, almost a ghost of a ghost. I walked back to the stairs. It was then I realised I'd been holding my breath and let it out explosively.

I could lift a carving knife and feel its weight. I could open a door or walk through it as if it wasn't there. Walls could be as insubstantial as air or as solid as, well, a wall. I could, effectively, float above a hole and feel like I was standing on a floor. Ol' Patrick Swayze shouldn't have tried so hard in 'Ghost'.

I was dead. A phantom. Spectre, wraith, shade, whatever. I found I didn't mind. It had been a painless death, for which I was grateful (and surprised – from the state I was in below, I'd have thought it should have been excruciating). I wasn't sure what I should do now. Was this it for me? Was I destined to wander the Earth as a spirit? Could I think of any more melodramatic clichés? Perhaps this was death. Maybe, if I returned home, I'd meet other ghosts, maybe even everyone who had ever lived! I lived alone (apart from Tilly – who'd look after him?) and had no family to speak of so I wasn't really going to be missed. I was getting bored with my job anyway, so that was no great loss.

Thinking of work reminded me why I had originally come here. I'd forgone any thoughts of finding evidence of ownership, but figured I may as well look around again. I hadn't been to the first floor yet. I wondered if there would be a bed in one of the rooms, doubting it if the rest of the house was anything to go by. I wasn't tired, but if there was, I wondered if I could actually sleep. I climbed the stairs.

At the top was a small square landing, more a longer top step than anything else. It was perhaps two foot square and simply formed a gap between the two rooms that occupied the top floor. Doors, typically worn and beaten, led to either side and

I had a shiver of déjà vu as I mentally flipped a coin to choose a bedroom. Tails. I stepped right, not bothering to open the door. A chorus of voices rippled through me as my body and the wood mingled, and then I was through. Of course the floors and walls were bare, making the room almost identical to the two downstairs. A large window to the front allowed views of the fields I'd hiked through. I could just make out the road I'd left my car on far in the distance. A much smaller window was set in the sidewall – the "killer's window" I'd seen from the outside. The rear wall was plain. I returned to the landing and entered the next room. Again my body echoed with sound. This second room was a mirror image of the first. The windows to the front and side were identical, and once more the rear wall was windowless.

I looked out of the side window. I could see the curve of the inlet and the fog that embraced it so closely - the fog that was as still as if it were a solid mass, and hid so many horrors.

I gasped. The wolves! I'd forgotten about the wolves! How did I forget them? How could I leave here with them prowling around outside?

Oh, I thought, running my hand through my hair. I'm a ghost. Even if they could sense me in some innate animal fashion, or knew I was there, they couldn't exactly tear me limb from limb – I didn't have any now! I returned to the stairs, the voices seeming a touch more insistent as I passed through the door. I walked down the stairs and along the hallway, across the hole in the phantom floor as if it was still present and into the kitchen. I stood at the window and stared into the fog. It trembled and convulsed as if alive – I could almost hear it scraping across the glass as it moved.

Suddenly, hovering at roughly head height, was a pair of red eyes. They looked like someone had cut the mist and blood was seeping out in a slash of colour. I stepped back involuntarily then remembered that whatever was out there couldn't hurt me. I moved back and returned the gaze. My face was inches from the glass, my hands leaning on the edge of the sink. I was trying to see the body of the wolf, thinking it so strange that I could only see the eyes then, in true Cheshire Cat style, a maw opened beneath them. Teeth longer and sharper than any mere wolf's leered at me and a snarl reverberated through the glass, making it shake in its frame. Then the mouth was gone and, a second later, the eyes disappeared too. A shape moved in the fog and then it resumed its incessant churning. I was shaking. Even with the knowledge that the creature (it couldn't be a wolf, but I didn't know what it was) could do nothing to a ghost, I was unsettled. It had looked directly at me, and it had threatened me.

I was breathing heavily. My heart was pounding and I was trembling. It took an effort to settle my nerves.

This was no good, I scolded myself. I was dead! I couldn't die twice! They could threaten me and even try to attack me, but I wasn't really here! Their teeth would just bite through me. I had a mental image of a wolf-like beast uselessly snapping at my body while I looked on and laughed. I liked that picture. That would get them back for trying (and succeeding) to scare me! I walked to the back door and pulled it open, smiling.

The smile froze on my lips as what seemed like hundreds of shapes lunged at the open doorway – at me. I fell backwards and kicked the door shut. It bounced open again, hitting one of the creatures.

And I was face to terrible face with terror.

The eyes seemed torn into a skull that looked like it may once have been human, but now was contorted out of shape – stretched to give it a snout. The ears were sharp and flat against the head and a lank mass of hair clung along the centre. Double rows of sharp incisors snapped as the maw opened and closed hungrily and fetid breath grazed my cheeks. A solid neck, traced wildly with muscle and vein, merged into a powerful body that hung low to the ground on all fours. I glanced down at the feet and saw long fingers with equally long talons. They looked more like hands than an animal's paw! The beast was still outside, staring at me as if giving me time to consider my impending death, perhaps not realising, or caring, that I was already dead. I took my chance and leaped at the door, pushing it shut hard. Before it closed completely, the brute's paw jabbed out, slashing at my arm.

I screamed in agony as the nails sliced into my arm and the creature shrieked in mutual pain as its entire leg burst into flames. The door clicked shut and I lay clutching my savaged arm, sobbing. Outside, something dreadful howled and beat against the door. Somehow, as before, the door held.

I crawled away from the exit and leaned against the sidewall. Gritting my teeth, I drew my hand away from my wound... to find there was nothing there. My shirtsleeve wasn't ripped, my arm wasn't a shredded mess. I could feel where there should have been gashes raked across, the skin hanging and the bone exposed. If I closed my eyes I could almost see it. But I was a ghost! Ghosts weren't real – weren't tangible. How could I feel pain? How could that creature have seen me, let alone attacked me?

My arm burned white-hot fire. I moaned, feeling lost and pathetic. I didn't understand any of this. Nothing. I just couldn't understand!

I think I may have passed out. It was dark when I next opened my eyes. The pain in my arm had receded somewhat and was now a sharp ache, much like the retching feeling that hung in my stomach like... a bad curry. That was how I felt – as if I'd eaten something that really didn't agree with me. Not that I'd be eating anything anymore. I looked at my watch and was shocked to see that around a week had passed since my run in with whatever waited for me outside. It was well past midnight and the house was silent. I could hear no wind or creak of settling wood. I turned my head to the back door. All was quiet. Somehow, that wasn't very comforting. I suddenly felt very uneasy – vulnerable - sitting there in the dark. I had been unconscious, or whatever dead-equivalent state compared, for six days. The thought of that and the realisation that only a rotten wooden door stood between a horde of monsters and me, made me feel sick. I needed to move. I could think of nowhere safer than a room with no doors and crawled (not trusting my legs to hold me) through the wall to the room beyond.

The voices were virtually shouting my name as I passed through the wall. That, along with a myriad other sounds, created a cacophony that was just too much and I collapsed through it onto the floor on the other side. Again I may have, must have, passed out. It was light when I woke. I checked my watch. It was mid-morning and around three weeks had passed. Well, I thought, at least three weeks had passed. It could have been months for all I knew. My head ached, but my arm was more or less OK now, the throbbing was no little more than a dull twinge.

I needed to get out of here. I had an almost irresistible urge to run straight out of the house. I could open doors and lift knives, so maybe I could even go as far as being able to drive my car, if it was still parked on the road. Of course, a mad sprint across the fields was not such a good idea with dozens of jaws snapping at my heels, but staying here was not an option. I had to get out.

I pushed myself, with some effort, to my feet and looked out of the window. It was a bright day. The grass was long and flowing freely in a mild breeze. Wispy clouds skittered across an otherwise clear sky. I suddenly longed to feel the warmth of the sun on my face, but wasn't sure if I'd be able to enjoy even that small luxury. I had to stop myself walking to the front door – I hardly needed to take that route now – and stepped to the window. I paused, wondering if I was being idiotic. I was safe in here, for now at least.

That was what made up my mind. 'For now.' I didn't know how long the door would hold them back. It, like the rest of the house, wasn't strong. It was a wonder how it had withstood the battering for this long. I could wait where I was or leave now and be attacked either way. I may as well try my luck outside.

I hesitated again. One thing played on my mind. Why had the creature's leg caught fire after it had struck me? Was it some sort of immediate allergic reaction to me? I doubted that somehow. I didn't have any skin or blood anymore, unless it didn't particularly like 'ectoplasm', or whatever I might be made of now. Perhaps it had something to do with the cottage itself? But what? I shook my head. I didn't know and there was no way I could find out. I wasn't prepared to offer myself up as the main course to find out either. Staying where I could only postpone the inevitable, I was sure.

The urge to flee blindly had faded, but I knew I had to leave. The window would provide no resistance. I could simply walk forwards and be out of here. I may even be lucky and not attract the attention of those beasts.

So I did.

I stepped forward and rested my hand on the glass. It felt cold. Maybe I would feel the sun's heat. I dropped my arm and walked... into the window! Not through it, into it! I tried again, and a third time. Nothing. It was like walking into a balloon – the glass would give slightly, bending outwards as I pushed, but something prevented me from passing through it. I struggled to keep calm. Perhaps there was something about glass that... No, that was ridiculous. Wood, glass, brick – I was a ghost. It was all the same, surely!

The front door. That would work!

I turned and ran towards the hallway. I could feel a sense of panic creeping at the back of my mind. I wanted to escape before it took hold and made me do something stupid. Escape. That was what I was trying to do. I suddenly felt a prisoner.

I was moving through the wall. Abruptly I stopped, or rather was stopped. I couldn't move. It was as if my body and the wall had become one – had merged as I stepped through. No, that was wrong. I wasn't part of the wall. My body hadn't solidified. I was being held. I could feel it, like a clamp around every part of me – I was a prisoner. But why? How?

And where were the voices?

As if on cue, they started. The raucous clamour that had accompanied each of my previous encounters was gone. It seemed the house had me now – I was a captive audience, and it didn't need to shout.

Whispers.

I could hear my name over and over, almost a chant. A song, somehow familiar, became entwined with my name, giving the mantra a melody. The hallway (my head, like the rest of me, was half in the room and half in the hall) began to fade to be replaced by a soft blue river that flowed across my eyes. I felt relaxed and strangely calm.

After a while the voice repeating my name became more insistent, emphasising the syllables. It grew louder, drowning out the song until it was almost shouting at me. The blue river became a violent torrent and I squeezed my eyes, futilely, shut. Even with them closed, the deluge continued. The din increased until I couldn't take anymore.

"WHAT?" I shouted.

The sound ceased. The river slowed, then stopped. I realised I was panting.

"What?" I asked quietly.

I heard my name.

"Yes," I said.

The song began again and the waters of the river parted to show the house with the Moors behind. The house in this image was in much better condition than it now looked. The fence was straight and complete and the front door looked almost new. The picture blurred slightly then focussed to show the nearby village. It seemed to be a live picture, as I could see cars and people moving about. The view changed again and I saw another town, not one I recognised. This, too, appeared to be live as people milled about their daily lives, oblivious to the dead person watching them. The town became indistinct and then settled on the house once more.

I frowned, not sure of what I was being shown.

"And?" I asked the air.

The river surged suddenly and the song became momentarily angry. Then it calmed and I got the sense of a deep breath being taken somewhere close by.

"Who are you?" I asked.

The water became the house.

I repeated my question. The image shifted and stilled. It was the house.

"You are the house?" I didn't understand. The house was talking to me? Had my recent demise sent me mad?

The melody quietened briefly, as if considering an answer. The figure of the house remained and I felt an indecisive confirmation, like whatever it was couldn't quite put into words, or pictures, what it was trying to say. I suddenly felt a pressing sense of impatience and the house itself shook – a rumble rising from its foundations.

As if someone was slowly turning up a volume control, the song, my name and untold other noises grew in number and degree as the river again became a deluge. Whatever was holding me and showing me these images and sounds had passed the point of trying to do it gradually. I suddenly felt like a baseball hit to a home run. My senses were overwhelmed as the house practically screamed at me.

At first I couldn't make any sense of what I was being shown. Images overlapped and blurred into each other at an astonishing rate, and the voices, music and other sounds merged into a solid block of noise. I could feel my body shaking in the house's vice-like grip. Then, I don't know whether the onslaught subsided to some extent, but I began to be able to pick out the odd scene and sound. Some were linked, but most were a jumbled mass until, gradually, they seemed to level out – to reach a plateau of some sort and I could finally understand them.

As my grasp resolved, the display returned to the beginning.

I was shown the house. I was shown its history. I was shown the true nature of the wolves and why I was now dead. I was shown the future.

The house was a force. That was the closest term I could relate to. It was more than alive and still not precisely living. It had consciousness but not thought. It didn't have true shape but, needing physical form, had 'become' the house. A building conformed to the current nature of Man. A building would be safe.

Previously, for an aeon, it had been a vast oak, twice the height of the house with sweeping branches half again the length of the fence. It had filled this cove in the coastline of the Moors. Before that, for longer than could be measured, it had been a huge block of stone, a massive obelisk that looked carelessly dropped by the same child that had tossed my corpse into the cellar. Its shape had changed with time, as Man had changed. The enormous mass of rock had become the oak when Man had fashioned the tool. It had become the cottage when Man had abandoned his respect of nature, favouring material possessions.

It did this because it needed to be... indefinite. It had to last a lifetime – not the lifetime of one person, but the lifetime of the world. It was a barrier, a boundary between what I had to call 'my' world, and another, much darker, world. This wasn't, from what I could discern, anything like a different dimension. I didn't have the lead role in some sort of science fiction film, however much I might wish I had. This other 'world' was more a different aspect or facet of mine. It was a shadowy domain of demons and terror.

The force that held me prevented the two from converging. That was why the demons, which I finally understood the crimson eyed wolves to be, beat against the back door. They were trying to break down the barrier – to gain access to that which was forbidden them. If they succeeded, well, I was shown that too.

The demons didn't care whether their victims were alive or dead, real or a ghost. It was simply prey.

They would tear a person apart if they were living, and then do the same to their spirit. My arm had been an insignificant example of this. I was, in part, protected in here. Outside, and without the protection of the house, I would no longer exist, ghost or otherwise – I could, it seemed, die twice. The demons didn't discriminate between people or animals – in fact, anything living was prey.

And it wasn't a hunger for them. They didn't attack, maim and kill absolutely, out of some instinctive desire for survival. The demon horde, thousands upon thousands of the lupine beasts, killed because they could. The living couldn't see them, and were torn asunder by an unseen monster. For the dead, it was much worse. The dead had no defence. The dead could see their attacker. The dead could die.

"Why me?" I asked. What could I do? I was a phantom now. Even if that wasn't the case, I was defenceless.

Then that, too, was revealed.

The house – the force that bound me – knew the reason I had come here. It had seen that I (or the Company I worked for) sought to develop this land, and that meant its destruction. There was no way it could allow that. It hadn't, I knew, killed me out of spite or retribution – it had done so because it needed me to know. The development had to be stopped and the only way it could warn me was for me to die.

It was absurd. It was so obviously absurd. I could laugh if I wasn't so totally horrified.

It thought I could help. It believed, if I knew, I could stop the work. It thought I could help.

It didn't understand that, as a ghost, I was near useless. I could feel its confusion. I tried to explain that the people who would come wouldn't be able to see or hear me. I could stop them no better than I could stand in the way of the demons.

The house began to shudder. A booming growl shook the walls and broke the spell I was under. The house released me and I fell back into the room. I looked about me and realised the vibrations were not coming from the walls. The ground itself was shaking. I ran to the window.

I banged against the glass. I shouted until I was hoarse. I waved my hands frantically.

It was useless.

The driver of the bulldozer was Tom. I knew him well. I'd been to his daughter's christening only three months previously. Her name was Kia and she was the spitting image of her mother, Tom's wife Diane.

I could see, wandering around with his mobile phone permanently attached to his ear as usual, the foreman. Chris was a nice guy, if a little absent-minded. He was single, but had twin sons, Chris Junior and Jack (or John, I couldn't quite remember). He saw them at the weekends.

I dropped my arms to my sides. I closed my mouth. I stood and stared silently as Tom drove the bulldozer at the fence, crushing it like paper.

He didn't slow as the house groaned its despair.

He didn't slow as, beyond the back door, thousands of demons, vaguely wolfish with crimson slashes for eyes and claws and faces that were almost human, bayed in guttural delight.

The howls and snarls increased in volume and ferocity as the bulldozer neared the house.

Chris had, for about the first time since I'd known him, put away his phone. His large team of workmen surrounded him. Various items of plant machinery and vehicles dotted the fields behind them. Half a dozen or so steel frameworks had already been erected, creating a spider-like village of metal.

Chris and his men looked on as Tom, who drank 2 pints of bitter every Friday night and simply loved fish and chips, drove his bulldozer into the front of the small, ramshackle, run down old house that no-one owned or really even cared about.

The demons, I realised, had fallen silent.

They were waiting.

Shaun Allan

Feel

I don't feel angry at what you did to me.
The rage has gone, the fury past,
The hatred just a sad, sad memory,
I don't feel angry.

I don't feel glad for what you left with me,
The scars that shadow the deepest cuts,
The twisted echo of what was my heart,
I can't feel glad that you tore me apart.

I don't feel sad that you're no longer close to me,
That I won't feel your presence in the dark,
That I won't have your smile, your eyes, your arms,
I won't feel sad.

Can't you see what is left of me?
Don't you know what you have done?
Won't you see what my smiles conceal,
That now you have gone
I won't, can't, don't feel.

I just don't feel.

Shaun Allan

The Silence

Modified Radical Mastoidectomy.

Trying saying that with a mouth full of Maltesers after five pints of vodka. Bet you can't.

My ears are knackered. That's the deal. A defect from when I was born that meant the canals joining all my nasally-ear bits together decided they didn't want to grow past me being 3 years old.

This will sort it all out. After a life of infections and partial hearing, I'll have a little less hearing but no infections. Well, half the time I don't particularly want to hear what people say anyway. I much prefer to be lost in my books. Escaping to worlds and lives far removed from my humdrum existence.

Sometimes I wish I could sail along the canals that I'm having repaired, perhaps on a Venetian gondola - they do, after all, feel like they're full of water half the time.

I'm going down to theatre in a few minutes. They're coming to take me away, ha-ha. The line will be going in and I'll be off to sleepy-byes...

* * *

Wha...? Where...?

Oh. That's right. I'm in hospital. There's a huge pressure on my head. Bandages are wrapped around me. They're covering my eyes too. I was expecting some padding over my ears, but not this. Surely it's overkill? I panic for a moment, but soothing hands pat my own, stroke my arms.

Calm down, they're reassuring me. It's ok.

I suppose it is. I should have asked about it, really. Not assumed. Saying that, maybe they should have told me. Either way, it is too late now. I am a mummy - or at least my head is. Part of the walking dead. Ancient beyond words and twice as crumbly.

Well, I can't see so at least I can entertain myself with silly thoughts. I picture myself walking around, arms outstretched, groaning - just my head swathed but the rest of my body joining in the fun.

I can't hear anything. I expected that. At first, at least. There would be swelling, internally and externally. It would be a day or two before sounds would seep in. But the pain and the headaches and the constant infections would be gone.

I could handle a couple of days of deafness for that.

It's not fun when you're being fed and you can neither see nor hear. The nurse's fingers (I assume it's a nurse and not some random person stalking the halls of the hospital shovelling food into patients mouths) are tapping my mouth for me to open it for the spoon. I don't like tomato soup and I've tried to say as much. They're still feeding it to me, though. I feel like a baby being weaned.

Maybe I am. Just missing the nappy.

* * *

The bandages are coming off. Finally. I didn't expect it to take three days but perhaps I haven't healed as fast as they'd hoped. I think it's been three days, anyway. I've slept at odd times. When you're surrounded by the night, it's hard to know when it's actually day.

I feel like I've been carrying someone on my shoulder for too long, and they've just climbed down. As the bandages come off, I feel like I'm floating. I'm levitating off the bed and they'd best watch out before I drift out of the window.

I know to be careful. Three days of darkness means I must take it slowly opening my eyes. I do. Easy does it. A crack at first. Blinking. Oh, it hurts. Even though it appears to be evening, it's a vast contrast to blindness. Still, it's good to be able to see again.

Blurry shapes. Figures. A face, I think. Yes. A face, closing in. Smiling. The doctor. My vision is clearing. That's better.

I smile back.

The doctor's mouth is moving, but I can't hear anything. Perhaps I still have padding over my ears. I can still feel the bandages around my face, even though they're not there. I reach up to my ears.

Nothing there.

I frown. I should be able to hear something, shouldn't I? Not as much, I know, but something?

I say that I can't hear anything. I don't know if I shout it or not. Tough if I do, really. Even my own voice betrays me - it isn't echoing inside my head. Has the silence snatched it away? Eloped in the night for a frantic shotgun wedding at Gretna Green? Or Vegas if they can afford the flights?

The doctor is frowning. He says something to me. I have no idea what and he seems not to realise that I need to be able to hear to be able to hear him. He leaves the room. I assume he is going to investigate, though my ears are in here, with me. Attached to my head as they always have been.

I'm ok. No need to panic. Maybe the swelling is still too much. The sounds can't squeeze through the gap to play tom-tom on my inner ear.

A whisper. I'm sure I hear a whisper.

I turn my head. It is coming from my left. There's nothing there. Only the shadows as the light fades. There is only the lamp above my bed to shed any light in the room. The door is closed and lets in barely a glimmer through the frosted glass.

My imagination is playing tricks on me. I want to hear so much, I'm having phantom sounds, much like if I'd lost a limb. My attention returns to the door. The doctor will be back in a moment.

Movement. Like a slither. A smooth sound. On the floor. I lean over, half expecting to see snakes crawling out from beneath my bed. There is nothing. Only a deepening darkness.

I cough, deliberately, to see if any part of it manages to invade my head and prove to myself that I am not hearing things.

Perhaps I'm mute too. I've been blind and deaf, so third time is the charm.

But I know I'm not. I can feel the vibration of my voice in my throat. I know it is there, hanging in the air before my face, pulling a moony at me.

The whisper again. It's on the left. No the right. Directly in front of me.

But nothing is there. I can see only shadows.

Off to one side is the television. It's on a long arm that allows it to be pulled over the bed. I do so and press the button to switch it on. After a brief advertisement encouraging me to buy credit to call the outside world or add more channels, a program appears. It's a soap. I don't watch soap operas, feeling that life is easily more entertaining in all its many colours. I leave it, though. It sheds a little luminosity. There's sound, of course, but it is currently redundant.

The television is actually making me more nervous. The flickering glow is causing the shadows to dance on the periphery of my vision.

Again, I hear the whisper. It's not in my head. I know it's not. It's real. The mouths on the actors move, but nothing is coming out. I press the Volume Up button. Still, an absence of noise.

Except for that whisper.

And the slither.

My heart leaps as the door opens and the doctor returns. He's holding a folder. My notes. He says something to me again then finally gets the point when I shake my head.

He pulls out a pen and writes on the folder, showing it to me.

"Not sure of problem. Should have worked. Probably swelling. Will fix. Don't worry"

The whisper. Not just an indistinct murmur now.

<worry... worryworryworry...>

It is coming from everywhere. Where there are shadows there is sound. Where there is light, only silence.

I take his hand, gripping the wrist.

Let me out, I plead. I can hear sounds. Not voices, just... sounds.

He nods and smiles. A thumbs up. Then he leaves.

NO! Not those sounds! Come back!

<back.... come back...>

A pause. I stare into the shadows. They stare back at me.

You

I wanted your world in the palm of my hand,
I wanted your life to be mine on demand,
I thought you needed my every movement,
My breath and my taste and my sense.

It was so easy to say it was me and not you,
So easy to doubt, so easy to hate,
So easy to accept what I did to you,
So easy to say it was fate.

But it wasn't, was it? It's not gone as we said,
If it was, I wouldn't feel like crying, like dying,
At the emptiness in my bed and my head.

I thought I was the best that you'd had,
My ego, my arrogance,
You turned it around.
Now that I'm falling, my folly I've learned,
I dream that I'm hitting the ground.

No-one can touch me, no-one can get in.
I'm my own succour, it's myself I believe in.
Need is no part of me, there's no room in my heart,
So why does the thought of you tear me apart?

Shaun Allan

The Glass

She looked deep into the mirror, wondering...

The wrinkles. Are they really as bad as they look? Laughter lines, surely, though she couldn't remember anything being THAT funny. The hair. A little tug here, a little push there. Thankful that red hair doesn't really go grey. A pout of the lips, the two cigarettes a day not enough to make the pout look like a crater, all ridged and rough.

The ear rings. A bit too much, really. She never, ever wore large hoops like that usually. She didn't even know why she had them in today. Why not? The same reason she wore the simple white training shoes instead of the heels. The jogging suit rather than the black trousers or skinny jeans she favoured.

Dress Down Day. She tried to have one every month, a cure for the chaos of her life. Work, no rest and very little play. Without her DDDs, she felt she'd go insane. A break. A breath. Chance to scratch her behind without feeling she was wiping everyone else's.

So. Why not the hoops. A little much, but still, not the small plain studs she felt she was required to wear.

Some habits were hard to break. The hair for example. She regarded herself in the mirror. It was just too set. Too right. With a sigh she pulled the grips holding the perfect bun in place.

"Stop it," she muttered to herself. "Dress DOWN day!"

She smiled. She had a pretty smile, she thought. Her eyes still sparkled at the rise of her mouth, just as they did a good twenty years or so before. She'd never lost the sparkle.

She picked up an elastic hair bobble from the dressing table by her side and scooped her hair back. A simple pony tail. Why not.

"You'll do," she told her mirror-self.

She turned and walked to the door, picking up her phone on the way. It was also her mp3 players and library, thanks to the music and eReader apps she'd installed. A run, a read and a relax. Perfect for a Triple D.

Her hand was on the door. Something was troubling her. A niggle nudging at the back of her mind like a kitten wanting a bowl of milk.

She turned back to the room, scanning across it. The usual mess of discarded clothes and shoes covered the floor, an assault-course of attire that made getting to the bed in the dark a dangerous undertaking. The bed itself had once been made. The quilt had been straightened and the cushions set out so it looked like an oasis in a sea of insanity. That once was roughly about six months previously. Apart from a casual tidy when the bedding was changed, the bed did its very best to match the rest of the room.

She liked to call it 'lived in.'

Nothing was out of place. Rather, everything was out of place, which meant it was all IN place. She shrugged.

She opened the door. Normally, she'd walk along the short corridor, picking up her keys from the wooden bowl on the small table along the way. She'd grab a coat if necessary (which it wouldn't be today as the one day of summer a year had decided today, you lucky people, was the day), and she'd be out of the front door.

It took a moment for her eyes to adjust to what she was seeing, and a longer moment still for her mind to adjust to what she wasn't.

Then she vomited. The remains of her breakfast, cereal and toast washed down with a tepid tea, were launched into the corridor. Or what was meant to be the corridor. What was supposed to be. What she remembered it being.

But what was actually...

It started off fine. The big, brash patterned wallpaper. The chrome light switch not quite seated correctly so it clung to the wall at a slightly skew-whiff angle. For a foot or two, anyway.

Then the hallway became a sickening whirlpool of tortured flower wall print and beige carpet that spun off to, well, forever. She felt she was hanging over an abyss, one that was ready to suck her from her feet and swallow her along with the hall.

She slammed the door and fell backwards onto the floor, cushioned by a fallen cushion and the previous day's cardigan. She wiped her mouth and stared, unseeing, at the remains of puke that ran up her wrist. After a few deep breaths had steadied her (though a vodka might have had more effect), she pushed herself to her feet and returned to the door.

She turned the handle and pulled.

Swirling, yawning maw. Colours merging to an indescribable mess.

And breathe.

She took a step forward. It was her imagination. She gulped to hold back the vomit. Her hand lifted to flick the light switch, but there was no bulb - or ceiling - to respond.

She was standing on the small part of the floor that was still in one piece. Keep walking. It's not real. Ten paces and you'll be at the table. Another two and it's the door. Go.

GO.

She lifted her foot and slowly moved it forward, only to see it lengthen and join the whirlpool before her. Her leg felt like a hundred hands were dragging down the flesh, pulling it away into the void. She held back the vomit, but fell backwards again.

This time there was no cushion to protect her. Her backside landed on one of her copious shoes that were strewn across the floor. She didn't feel it. She was too busy touching her leg, frantic to make sure it was still in one piece. To make sure she kicked out, slamming the door once more.

A moment passed. She could feel her thoughts whirlpooling like the chasm beyond the door. She looked around. There was no other way out.

Wait.

The window.

Rising slowly, unsteady on a leg that she wasn't yet sure was still attached properly, she moved to the window. It was a first floor flat; she would have no problems climbing out and hanging down, dropping to the ground.

She looked out. All seemed right with the world. It was a typical Sunday morning. Cars were driving by. People were walking. Talking. Some holding hands, some on their phones, some huddled down, hands in pockets.

The window was locked. It always had been. She'd never had reason or inclination to open it. The key. The key...

Ah.

On her dressing table was a small lidded pot. In it was a jumble of hair clips, a spent battery, and the key to the window lock. Rather than fumble, she up-ended the pot and emptied the contents onto the table. She expected to need to search, but the key lay on top, almost wanting to help her escape.

Thankful, she snatched it up and slipped it into the lock, surprised at herself that she managed it with shaking hands. There was a soft click. She turned the handle and pushed.

Her breath was yanked from her lungs as the world outside changed suddenly from the street she knew to the vortex in the hall. Again the colours were thrown together, melting into one another. She could see faces and cars and buildings, but they were stretched and fused together. She held onto the sill and looked from this new Outside to the window.

Through the glass she should still see the street. People still walked. A dog pulled at its lead. Someone was talking to a driver that had pulled over to the kerb. They were laughing.

She pulled the window shut. The world beyond went on, ignorant to the shock on her face. Oblivious to the high mewling that she didn't realise was coming from her mouth.

She stepped back. What? Why? How could she SEE the world but not ENTER it? What had happened to the hall? Outside? Why could she see it through the glass.

The glass.

An idea stole into her mind, creeping through the confusion then slipping away before she could quite grasp it.

She looked at the window again and then ran her fingers along it. She could see the street. She could see the reflection of her bed and the clothes on the floor.

But she couldn't see herself.

It occurred to her that she might be a ghost. She'd died in the night. Her body would be on the bed, still looking like it was sleeping peacefully. She turned and looked. The bed was empty.

Her gaze returned to the window and she waved her hand. Her lack of reflection didn't wave back.

A movement out of the corner of her eye.

The mirror.

She turned quickly, but could see nothing but her room. But...

She walked slowly over. The room in the mirror expanded as she moved closer. She could see... herself. But it wasn't herself. It was someone who looked like her, but that someone wasn't standing at the mirror looking back. That someone was on her phone, talking. It would be Ed, her boyfriend. She always spoke to him before her jog. She always...

What did she do? She couldn't quite remember. The hall. Outside. It had jumbled her mind, casting her thoughts aside like clothes on the floor.

Surely.

The call was ended. The her in the other room walked to the door and turned the handle.

She screamed out. "No! Don't go out there!"

But in the mirror, she could see the hallway. She could even, if she moved her head over to the edge, see along it to the corner of the table. It was all as it should be.

She didn't have a reflection. She didn't have a world outside this room.

She banged on the glass.

"Come back! Don't leave me!"

Other her walked out into the hallway, pulled the bedroom door closed.

"No!!"

The door clicked shut.

She looked around at her own door. Longing. Wishing.

Then her world - her reflected version of the real world beyond the mirror glass - disappeared until the real her ventured into the room again and the reflection was needed once more.

"No..." she whispered in the darkness.

Shaun Allan

Look For Me

Look for me in the sea of faceless faces.
Look for me in the empty soulless wastes.
Look for me in the barren, hopeless places,
And in the cruel and heartless traces.

When you feel the confines closing,
When you see the bridges collapsing,
When you hear the thunder crashing,
Look for me.

I am your shadow.

I am your darkness.

I am your light.

I am your friend.

Shaun Allan

There Be Dragons

That's how the dragons get in and out. My cousin told me so.

I think I was 9 at the time. He was older than me. 16 and loving scaring his younger protégé. Of course I believed him. I also believed in Santa and the Tooth Fairy.

Even now, an adult, I can't sit in the bath with my back to the taps. I have to be facing it. I have to be able to keep watch on it.

At the sink, it's the same - though I don't get a bath in the basin. But, when I'm brushing my teeth or washing my face, I'm always a little wary.

The overflow. A little hole (or group of holes with the grill on the bath). An innocent aperture happily guzzling the excess water from when you fill up the sink or bath too much.

The overflow. Dragon swallowing entrance to the Underworld.

You'd think that, now I'm all grown up, it wouldn't worry me. You'd think I'd be fine. Technically, it's just a hole to prevent the water overflowing. It kind of does what it says on the tin - or the ceramic. It's nothing. A rather ingeniously simple method of ensuring you didn't have to swim out of your bathroom.

What is there to be afraid of, hmmm?

Well. There's the voices, of course.

Low. Not much more than a whisper. Just enough to be able to understand what they say.

Voices that tell me I'm going to die. Voices that tell me my world is going to end. Not the world. My world.

Subtle, yet significant, difference there.

I'm not paranoid. I don't hear voices. OK, perhaps I do. But I mean, I am not one of these fruit-loops who say the voices in their head are telling them to take a knife to their wife. Or a gun to the local shopping centre. I'm not a lunatic.

Besides, the voices are not in my head, so I can't be crazy.

They're in the overflow.

No, really.

Of course, I don't really believe there be dragons in that there overflow. Not at all. I told you, I'm not crazy. That'd be silly. Besides, it's too small to fit a fully grown, fire breathing dragon in there. But there ARE voices.

The first time I heard them was about three weeks ago. It was morning. I was brushing my teeth, probably wondering if the cup of tea I'd already made was going to be too cold. I often did that. Made a cuppa and got so tied up in doing 'stuff' that it wouldn't be warm enough to drink by the time I got back to it.

I was spitting and rinsing. Leaned over. There was no 'Hello, how are you?' or any such introduction.

"You're going to die."

Succinct, don't you think? Why use ten words or more, when a snappy little phrase would do just as well.

I almost hit my head on the tap, I stood so fast. I looked around. I was alone in my house. My wife had taken the children to school and I didn't have to leave for a good twenty minutes. Still, I looked out onto the landing.

"Hello?"

There was no answer. There wouldn't be. I'd imagined it.

Two days passed. Two silent days of normality, when I realised my mind had been playing tricks and was just trying to scare me, the little tinker.

Then.

"You're going to die."

It was evening. I was washing my hands after a particularly long stretch on the loo. Well, I will take my phone in there and jump between Facebook, Twitter and whichever book I'm reading at the time.

I froze, my eyes staring into my reflection's. Had I heard that? Again? Or was it a trick of the running water hitting the ceramic bowl? Sure. That was it.

I laughed to myself. Daft old bugger. Not that I'm particularly old, nor am I known to be daft, but I can admonish myself with the best of them. My mind was wandering and the spill from tap to sink had tripped it up as it went, that was all.

"You are going to die."

No amount of water sprinkling and tinkling on any surface is going to make sounds like that. It's not like a load of monkeys got together and, in lieu of some typewriters, decided to urinate in the sink, the resultant splatterings eventually forming actual words.

Not exactly Shakespeare.

Right. I wasn't home alone that time. My wife, Olivia, must have been messing about. Or one of the children. A bit of fun. Yeah, so funny I could die...

I grabbed the towel and walked out of the bathroom, drying my hands as I poked my head into each of the bedrooms.

All empty.

I frowned. Was I losing my marbles? Were they spilling out of my ears and bouncing across the floor? No. All faculties were in order, front and centre, standing to attention.

I went downstairs.

My children were watching television.

"Hi dad," they chimed in unison. I smiled. It was clearly neither of them

"Ollie," I said.

She turned. She was making the packed lunches for the next day. In one hand was the butter knife and in the other the half empty tub. Again, it couldn't have been her.

She must have seen there was something wrong as her expression changed to one of concern.

"What's wrong?" she asked.

Rather than say anything in front of my children - to worry them or have them think their dad was weirder than they already did - I nodded my head towards the door. She put the butter tub down and slid the knife into it. I watched it enter, wondering if it could enter my own flesh as easily.

What? Where did that come from?

I shook my head and went through into the hall, my wife following.

"Have the children been upstairs?"

Ollie smiled. "You know what they're like once they're lost in the TV. They only get up for food or toilet breaks. They haven't shifted since tea time."

She was right. The 'Hi dad' was more than I would normally have expected.

"Have you?" I asked, knowing she hadn't but needing an answer.

"No, love. I've been sorting the pack up."

I chewed my bottom lip. It was a nervous habit I thought I'd grown out of. Along with thinking dragons inhabited the bowels of my basin.

"Are you ok?"

I looked up, not realising I'd been looking down.

"I'm fine, babe. I thought I heard something. Thought they were messing about. It's OK. Long day."

"OK," she said. "I'll get the pack up finished, then the kids can go watch TV in their room and we can curl up on the sofa."

"Sounds good," I said, smiling.

We kissed and she returned to the kitchen. I stayed where I was for a moment, looking up the stairs. It was my imagination.

Idiot.

Right. Come on. I went back up to the bathroom and finished off. In silence. No voices or threats of death.

And none for another couple of days. In the lull before, I'd put it behind me. Pretended it hadn't happened. I couldn't do that now, though. I couldn't make out all was well when strange voices were foretelling my doom. But neither could I say anything.

"Hey, Ollie. I've been hearing voices from the overflow."

"Voices?"

"Yes, they're telling me I'm going to die."

Shaun Allan

It wouldn't go down very well. She knew about my problem with overflows and would think my childhood phobia was overflowing into my adulthood. Overwork. Stress. Insanity.

Olivia was a very understanding woman. She would do anything for me and would go out of her way to make sure I was happy. But I would guess she'd draw the line at the dragons.

She would worry. She would fret. She'd get those wrinkles on her forehead. Or she'd tell me to not be a Muppet and get a grip. Either way, I just couldn't figure out how to broach the subject in a reasonably sane way. So I kept as quiet as I hoped the voices would.

And they did. For two days.

I didn't know the deal with the two days. Did a dragon sleep for that long? Or was Pennywise the clown paying me a visit and that was when I fitted into his rota of sewer based scares?

"You're going to dieeeee."

At home, it was ok. Well, not ok, but... contained. The oddity, the fear, the madness. At home it was dealable.

At the cinema, when you go to the toilet after sitting in one place for the best part of three hours, things are a little different. It's more sterile. More space.

More overflows. More dragons.

More voices.

I'd hoped to not be alone in there. I wanted some company. That had to be the first time ever I wanted somebody to be standing at the next urinal. thankfully the dragons waited until I'd finished before voicing their concerns.

"You are going to die."

I stumbled back, my lower back making contact with the row of sinks behind me. I turned, aware that a half dozen overflows would be staring at me.

In a similar way to how my children almost always spoke in harmony, six voices spoke together.

One word.

"Die."

I ran out of there. Out of the cinema. Leaning on my car, panting. My heart threatening to explode in my chest.

Ollie caught up with me.

"What's wrong? You look like you've seen a ghost!"

<Voices are coming out of the overflows. They're telling me I'm going to die.>

"No, no. I'm fine. The smell in there. Someone hadn't flushed. I thought I was going to be sick."

Ollie put her arms around me.

"You sure you're ok?"

I've never lied to my wife. Honesty had always been a major player in our relationship and we instilled it into our children. You don't get into trouble so much for what you've done as you do for being caught out lying about it.

"I'm sure."

A hug.

"Let's go home."

You'd think you can avoid bathrooms and sinks. Ignoring the fact that there's a sink in the kitchen, you can't. At some point you must brush your teeth. At some point you MUST relieve yourself in one way or another. I happened to hold off for two days.

I walked into the bathroom, forcing each step, pushing myself.

I did what I needed to do, then washed my hands.

I waited.

Silence.

With a breath deeper than my boots, I left the bathroom. Two days passed. Another visit. Another absence recorded on the register from the dragons. Perhaps they'd flown away. They escaped in the night and had found some other prey. I breathed easier. Another couple of days and another absence.

It was over. My senses had reconvened and had voted unanimously to behave themselves.

"You are going to die."

"Change the record, won't you? This is getting boring."

"You're going to dieeee."

"You've been telling me that for ages now. Clearly I'm not as I'm still living."

I'd had enough. Enough of thinking I was spiralling down the plughole of my reason. No more. Whatever these voices were, they'd obviously mixed me up with someone else. I couldn't be going to die or I'd be dead.

And I wasn't. My children and my wife still spoke to me, so I wasn't a ghost. I had become unexpectedly deceased and no-one had told me.

I'm going out. Ollie is picking the children up from their friends. They were going to spend the night, a sleepover, but the friend has suddenly started sprouting chicken pox. I think it's best ours stay there and have a pox party. Catch it now and get it out of the way. Ollie disagrees. She wins. As usual.

A short walk, that's all. It's dark but that's better. I don't have to hide the anger and frustration that must surely line my features. The night will mask it for me. The air hits me as I walk onto the path. Cool. Sharp, even. Blowing through me. It's invigorating. Life giving.

I'll walk along the river opposite. It's a good night to shove two fingers up to the dragons. The flow of water will help wash them away.

I look up just in time to see the headlights bear down on me. Too late to stop. Too late to swerve.

Thought is faster than any car or heartbeat. I have chance to wish that, if there were dragons in my overflow, it would be a good time to...

Shaun Allan

Time

Days fall into
Weeks fall into
Months fall into
Years.
Time passes in the blink of
The laughter, smiles and tears.

We wander through our lonely lives,
Struggling to achieve,
Knowing what we think we know,
Believing what we believe.

But still we try and halt it,
Keep it from its goal,
Ineffectually, knowing
It still will take its toll.

But that's because life is
Such a precious, short-lived time,
And short & lonely though it is,
It's all I have that's mine.

Fair of Face, Black of Heart

Of course, the darkest place of all is in a murderer's heart.

So they say.

The lifeblood that pumps around the body of a killer must be tainted. It must be a deeper shade of scarlet. Edging from deep red to black, night slipping into the liquid like a shadow drifting across the lawn as the sun sets beyond the horizon.

Would it be thicker than normal? Crawling rather than running through the veins and arteries? The evil of a murderer making it more viscous to match the viciousness of the deed?

No.

It isn't.

Blood is blood. Well, depending on which type of monkey you are, of course. Still, it's all blood. If you're a saint or a sinner, a monster or Mother Theresa, your own particular vintage of claret is much the same as the next person's. Granted, if you're dead, you'll be laying in a pool of it, as it seeps to the bottom of your body.

Well, if you're not walking around anymore, why should the blood? Not that it walks, exactly...

Jack laughed to himself. As a mortuary technician, his audience to these little jokes was less than lively. At least, he thought, he found himself funny. Sometimes he would have to stop what he was doing, hold the knife, as he made some mental quip or other that would set him off giggling.

It gained him a reputation as being a little odd. Laughing in the face of Death, whilst cutting open a cadaver, was frowned upon for some reason. But Jack would laugh at a funeral. In the most serious of situations, he couldn't help but have to suppress a snigger. It was his defence mechanism.

Well, it was nerves to be honest. The dead made him nervous.

One might think that a job in a mortuary might be an odd choice for such a man. One would be correct, but Jack had always thought himself to be somewhat left of centre. He was a loner, preferring the company of his thoughts to the chaotic ones of others. Thus he held the camaraderie of the deceased in high regard, however uneasy they might make him feel.

At least, though they didn't laugh at his jokes, neither did they deride his offbeat sense of humour.

He gave them names. Not necessarily the same ones as on the forms and wrist bands, but names anyway. He called them what he thought they looked like, believing they would have been that little touch lighter during life if only their name had matched their face. An Edward might have become a John. A Susan could be an Yvonne. They didn't seem to mind the change. They never complained, at any rate.

It had happened four years earlier. He'd only been a technician for a few months and was still getting used to being 'hands-in' with the cadavers.

He disliked the word. Cadaver sounded like the bodies were remnants, left over from a hyena's feasting. He preferred corpse. It at least gave some humanity to the person into whom he was placing his hands.

The body was that of a young man. He'd been brought in the night before. A crime had been committed, but Jack wasn't, as yet, a party to the particulars. He was there to photograph and to sample. He made the deep 'Y' incision and removed the ribcage, cutting it along the sides so that it would lift like the lid to a treasure chest, revealing the jewels hidden beneath.

He weighed and measured, and he made things ready for the pathologist.

Jack didn't aspire to that position. He didn't want the responsibility of giving causes or making choices and decisions. He was happy being the hand that helped. He enjoyed opening up the body to tell its tales and the closing of the curtains after the story was told.

The dead weren't his friends, but he felt welcomed by them.

He was fast, he was efficient and he was accurate. As such, he was left to his own devices much of the time in the knowledge that the way would be open for the real work to begin.

Four years. Time flies by when you're drinking rum, Jack's father used to say to him. Cirrhosis agreed and they went hand in hand to the great bottle in the sky.

It was late. The corpse had been waiting for a couple of days. The skin under the glaring lights was a vivid yellow, with the lower parts being purple where the blood had settled, chilling until such time as decomposition joined the party and they could putrefy together. The now familiar smell - cold meat, a metallic tang and antiseptic, bowels - did its best to defeat the Vapour Rub liberally applied to Jack's nostrils. It was a constant battle whose victor was never assured.

Brian was laid out on the body block. His head was back, the chest pushed forward. The photographs and samples from the extremities had been taken.

"I'm going in," Jack thought to himself. "I may be some time."

He laughed. Brian didn't.

The man was thick-set. He had a broad moustache that was sprawled across his top lip like a Lincolnshire Pork sausage that had been left for so long it had stumbled past mouldy and was now comfortably resting in hairy. Stubble sprouted across his chin and cheeks and his nose was a criss-cross of broken veins and pock marks.

His hands were immense and Jack could imagine them crushing anything that came close enough to be caught.

Brian, or Edward Corvak according to his wrist band, lay patiently for the first incision. Shoulders to sternum then down to pubis, kinking to the left of the navel. He didn't seem to mind either, being dead, when the ribs were cut for the removal of the chest plate.

Jack was still somewhat awed by this procedure. He felt as if he were gazing into Pandora's Box and all the evils of the world might spew forth. Secrets that should never be revealed could lie within the human form and Jack sometimes found himself talking to the corpse that he was eviscerating to calm it into not doing so whilst he was working.

Afterwards was fine. Unleash away, as long as he was elsewhere.

He was soon calmed, though, by the rainbow colours of the organs - an artist's tribute to the glory of nature.

The pericardial sac that housed the heart was waiting for him to knock on its door with his scalpel. Who was he to delay?

He first checked the pulmonary artery for a blood clot. It was clear, the walls a little thick, showing possible high blood pressure. At each stage, Jack spoke into his voice recorder, making copious notes. He was known, already, to be thorough and wanted to make sure he didn't miss anything. He felt it was better to record too much than too little.

The scalpel sliced into the pericardium easily, and Jack pulled it back to reveal the heart. From being a child, he had thought the human body - any body, in fact - to be a wonderful creation. Whether it was born of invention, evolution or accident, he didn't care, but he did have respect for its intricacies and its miracles. And at the heart of his wonderment was... the heart.

Without the heart to give the blood the kick up the corpuscle it needed to race through your veins your organs would pretty much suffocate. And you'd end up on the slab in Jack's hands.

His first thought was haemopericardium. A split in the aorta causing blood to surround the heart. The heart was black. Nothing wrong with that. It wasn't the first time Jack had seen hearts that appeared to be much darker than they should be.

But then there was a flicker. A shift. He looked up, thinking the lights had dimmed for a second. Someone had forgotten to put 50p in the electric meter, he murmured. The lights were steady. Their usual brilliance undiminished. He looked back down, blinking to help his eyes adjust.

Odd. The heart wasn't black anymore. It was its proper deep reddish-brown.

Oh well, Jack shrugged. On we go. Carefully but quickly, he removed the organs as one and laid them out for the pathologist to examine. Before long, he was finished and on his way home.

Edward Corvak. A lumbering brute. Hands that not only could crush, but did. It had started with animals. Small ones. He'd catch squirrels and mice. Squeeze them until they popped and crunched. As he grew, so did the size of his victims. Dogs. Cats. A sheep. If he couldn't hold the body, he was more than happy to squeeze the head. It took a little longer, and more force was required, but Corvak, one day to be called Brian, enjoyed a challenge.

He'd only killed three children before the blood clot reached his brain and the life he'd wrung out of so many others was snatched from him.

Jack woke sweating. The morning light streamed in through the wooden slats against his window, slicing his body into slivers of shadow. It took him a moment to realise he was shaking. It took another moment to realise why.

Jack didn't dream. Ever. Or rather, he didn't remember his dreams. Ever. He slept well and woke rested.

Must be that chicken he had last night. That'll be it.

A strong coffee and hot shower was enough to wash the nightmare from his mind and, by the time he was back at work, he'd forgotten it completely.

Until it came to putting the jigsaw that was Brian back together again. Then he couldn't help but look at the hands. He couldn't help but feel the weight of one, imagine it pressing down on his skull.

He shook his head and replaced the dead hand. It was a dream. Don't be daft. Get on with it.

Jack sighed, wiped his brow and proceeded to replace Edward Corvak's organs. Usually, he'd do his best, depending on the state of them post-examination, to rebuild the corpse to as close as nature intended as possible. It didn't really matter. Once the body was sewn back up nobody would know. Jack, however, had enough respect for both the deceased and for life itself, to honour the original design.

In the case of Corvak, Brian no longer, Jack just wanted the job done. The organs were returned to the cavity as they fitted, and if kidney shared personal space with lung then so be it. They'd have to learn to get along - at least until cremation quenched the fire of any argument they might have.

The dead made Jack uneasy. Edward Corvak, though he was no longer living and his innards (since being outards) were a jumble, scared him. He was relieved when the body was wheeled back into the freezer and he could move on to the next corpse.

Three months. Male. Jason/Phillip. A finger over 6 feet tall - or long, lying down. Incision, saw through the ribs, remove the plate, open the heart up.

Black. Like coal. Like shadows and space and the bit in the furthest corner under your bed, where you're sure there's a sock hiding but you just can't reach.

Jack gasped and Edward Corvak knocked on the door to his memory. Jack mentally locked the door, turning Corvak away and stared at the black lump before him. There was no potential flickering of lights, just a steady gaze in a brightly lit room.

The heart was black. Then it wasn't. Like a cover slipping from a bed, the blackness dissolved away, the heart returning quickly to red, though its edges were coated in yellowing fat.

Jack's heart fluttered in response, a hiccup in its rhythm.

No. A late night. An early morning. Tiredness and the beginnings of a headache. That was all. Dismiss, dismiss. Except it wasn't so easy this time. He could feel the memory of Corvak tip-toeing around his subconscious, but did his best to ignore him.

Get on, get on. Remove the organs. Lay them out. Clean. Weigh.

Jack did his best to avoid any thoughts of shadows on hearts or deceased murderers for the rest of the day and, that night, used vodka to wash away the remnants of the thoughts. It worked, vodka being a stronger warrior than his own psyche.

Until...

Jason. Or Phillip Tennison according to his birth certificate and his mother. A nice guy. Honest and polite and friendly. And then his wife died. A hit and run. Except he'd never had a wife. A few girlfriends now and then, but he was always too nice. Always too much of a friend to be a lover. What he did have was a chemical imbalance, precariously poised up to the point it slipped and fell and became a knife, slitting the throats of the raven-haired girls that resembled the non-existent wife who was so tragically torn from his side.

Jack wiped the sweat from his brow and the tears from his eyes. He waited for the shaking to subside and climbed out of bed, his legs unsteady as he turned the shower on full blast and full heat. In a daze, he was at work before he'd even realised he'd left his home.

What was going on? Why was he having these dreams? The dead had never affected him like this before. Why now? What was the deal with the hearts?

He thought of little more all day, the bodies before him being eviscerated without thought, his hands going where they should whilst his thoughts whirlpooled. He didn't even notice when the corpse he was stitching back together was Jason's.

A few days later, when the shock had faded and reality had steadied his unruly reason, Jack visited the optician. He must have something wrong with his eyes. He had a detached retina, which was it. It could be fixed. There had to be an explanation. A cure. He was seeing shadows where there were none and it was affecting his dreams.

Simple.

But the optician told him his eyesight was good. A mild hyperopia. Long-sightedness that was blurring things close up. Well, perhaps that was the answer? Maybe it was intermittent and that was causing...

... the black hearts and the dreams of death.

And the news had already told him his dreams were real. That Corvak and Tennison had indeed crushed and sliced. A minor eyesight issue could not explain that.

Four years in total. More than two dozen occasions. An opening. A black heart that changes quickly to red. A nightmare. Shooting. Stabbing. Rape. Strangulation. Kidnapping.

Not all appeared on the night-time news bulletins or in the newspapers. Not all the horrors came to light. But Jack knew. Jack saw. Jack felt and tasted and heard.

In a mortuary you become immune to many things. The smell of death, stomach contents, antiseptic and decomposition. The sound of a scalpel cutting through flesh or a saw cutting through bone. The sight of a body with its torso opened up and the organs removed. It becomes a job, in the end.

As it was with the black hearts and the nightmares. They were there. Jack could tell the police when he dreamt of a little girl being dragged into a car or an old man being beaten over the head by the teenager for a few coins. He could, but they'd want to know how. They'd think he was involved. Or guilty.

He kept his knowledge to himself. He accepted it. He knew that, when he cut the pericardium and peered inside, the shadow was that of evil. It was the taint of a devil or demon or whatever wickedness evil really was. And, when its job was done and the host was dead, the evil moved on.

Jack let it go.

Caroline. He had stopped giving them other names. Some, the killers, didn't deserve it. Given them pseudonyms was like giving them new identities. They should be known for who and what they were.

Caroline. In life she would have been attractive. Not the sort of girl to be called stunning or gorgeous, but Jack was certain she would have been seen as beautiful. She had graceful lines across her face and figure. She would have drawn stares of desire and jealousy and would not have noticed. It was a shame she had died. A loss to the world.

Incision. Chest plate. Pericardium. Evil, clutching the heart like Corvak would clutch a skull. A dark blanket of night. Of hate. Of murder.

Jack was furious, his acceptance turning to anger. Why defile someone who would not have even thought of committing a crime? Why pollute a person of purity? It was wrong.

And Jack realised why. Because. Just because.

The scalpel was still in his hand and he thrust it forward, piercing the heart, stabbing the mantle of malice. At first nothing happened, then a sharp jolt shot up his arm, knocking him back, releasing his grip on the blade.

A voice behind him: "Are you ok, Jack?"

The pathologist.

Jack reached forward and retrieved the scalpel. The pupils of his eyes were dilated, filling the iris with the same colour that had only seconds before been covering the heart in Caroline's chest.

He turned, a twisted smile on his face.

"Yes, Doctor Adams, I'm fine, thank you."

His hand whipped out, puncturing the left eye of his superior. The man fell backwards, screaming.

Jack advanced, blade held high.

"Everything is fine..."

Shaun Allan

Untitled

It's no longer warm
In your eyes that are a little colder
In the ocean that's no longer calm
In the face that, each day, seems a little older.

There's no longer space
In the heart that's a little harder
In the world that's, oh, so much smaller
In the void that reaches so much farther.

There's no longer peace
In the mind that's open no longer
In the soul that's fallen from grace
And in your eyes there's no longer a hunger

Joy

It's hard being me.

I'm sure I'm not the only one to have ever said that. In fact, I would think that someone is saying those exact words, or thinking the equivalent thought, right now.

Being anyone is difficult, I would think. Life is always tossing us a grenade to juggle, making us centre ring in the Big Top of our own little world. Will we stumble? Will we fumble? The spotlight is shining right down upon us, its beady eye waiting with bated breath to see what might happen.

Not that either spotlights or eyes have breath, bated or otherwise, but I'm sure you get my meaning. I'm not the weaver of words that my brother is. He can crochet a quilt of quips bedded upon a sea of sarcasm. I can't. But then, I didn't have the upbringing he did. He learned, long ago, that jokes were a better defence than his fists.

He wasn't a fighter, my brother, though he was dragged into enough scrapes to build up some small prowess. He learned to duck and to run, more than anything. And when he couldn't, he learned to block and to bounce. He could never, really, bring himself to retaliate. He accepted his fate.

With a name such as his, I'm not surprised. Our parents, our father mainly, took great pleasure in tugging at the immense weight they'd hung about his neck the day they named him. When the school bullies were bored with him and were looking elsewhere for their fun, our father, whose arse is likely not in Heaven, picked up their baton and ran with it.

I don't know about my brother, but I often wonder if they named him such just so they could keep themselves entertained for a few years.

Sometimes, I couldn't help myself. Sometimes I joined in. I'm not proud of that, but it's done now. We all do things we wished we hadn't, but sometimes that little imp gets into the back of your head and just gives you the right - or wrong - nudge. It had happened, admittedly, on more than one occasion, whilst growing up. I'd make fun of his name, goad him, even laugh as he was being beaten.

But I still loved him. He was my baby bro. We'd fall out and we'd bicker, but we were family.

Are family. Is my baby bro. Not past tense. Not yet.

I always knew I was different.

Again, that's something so many others will say and have said. But I was. People liked me.

Yes, I know. Why would that be such a bad thing? It shouldn't be. I should have enjoyed it, embraced it, but I didn't. Not that I was miserable - far from it. I was a fairly happy child. I didn't have the trouble my brother had. In fact, I almost think he sucked the problems from me before they could hit. Took them upon himself. Almost liking stopping a bullet for the president. I had an almost charmed life.

In complete contrast to his.

But it wasn't something I could control. I'd have given him some of my luck if I could have. Some of my... attraction? No, I didn't particularly think I was attractive, not particularly. Maybe pretty, but that was all. By 'attractive' I mean the way people just seemed to like me. They seemed to gravitate towards me, like I was a black hole and they were caught in my pull.

I'd have pushed if I could. Maybe my brother and I were polar opposites. I pulled, he pushed. Or was pushed, in a lot of cases.

I knew I was different. The bullies that beat my brother shouldn't have liked me. The dog that was ready to eat the postman's leg should have wanted my arm for dessert. But the bullies did and the Rottweiler didn't. And they went away with a smile on their faces. Even the dog. Not pretty...

It wasn't too long before I realised that it was the coin. The two pence coin.

See a penny, pick it up and all day long you'll have good luck. That's how the story goes, but not quite so the reality. I saw a two pence. I picked it up. And since then, since the first day, back in school, when I flipped the coin and caught it in the palm of my hand, everyone around me has had good luck.

In the hall at school. I was hall monitor, on 'corridor duty' with my friend Zoe. I had a little yellow house badge pinned to my school jumper. We were there to try and make sure that other pupils didn't run or fight. To be honest, we were there to be ignored. That was fine, we knew that'd happen. Or we'd be stood talking to our friends. It was just something to keep us in on the rainy days, really.

The coin was on the floor at my feet. I don't know how it got there. It certainly wasn't dropped, or I'd have heard it. Neither was it there when Zoe and I arrived, or I would have seen it.

Will Bronson, not quite the leader of the school Bully Brigade but certainly wanting to be, was picking on a second year.

The Bully Brigade was meant to be for seeking out and stopping any bullying. Certain pupils were asked to point out instances of schoolyard abuse to teachers. The fact that the upper echelons of the group were filled with the very folk they were meant to be dobbing in meant that the Headmaster could say there was no such thing as bullying at his school. When a thump or a kick were on offer as payment for pointing your finger, you kept your hand firmly in your pocket.

Will was a thug, and everyone knew it. That included the teachers and his parents. The former overlooked the situation in favour of another cuppa and Rich Tea biscuit in the staff room and the latter daren't say anything in fear of their son putting his foot through the television set. Or smashing all the plates in the kitchen. Or feeding their pet dog rat poison.

Though that had only happened once.

They were, however, on their third television in a year.

Zoe had called out to Will to leave the second year alone. We were in the same year as him and he liked my friend a little more than she liked him. In fact she didn't like him, but he decided not to notice. This one-sided attraction did, though, give her the authority to try and convince him to behave. He didn't take any notice, but at least he wouldn't turn his anger on her.

As she was telling him to stop, and he was ignoring her, I was bending down to pick up the coin that hadn't been there previously. My attention was on Zoe and Will. It wasn't until I felt the coin land in my hand that I realised I'd flipped it.

For some reason, I called out.

"Wilson!" Sniggers from the other pupils at my use of his full name - a practical hanging offence (a definite black-eye offence). A thunderous look from the bully. "Leave him alone."

Zoe and, I suspect, a number of others, stared at me. I felt my face flush. I can't say what prompted me to speak out, let alone use a name that had been scratched from every register in school.

Wilson's eyes locked on mine for a long moment and I could see the cogs grind in his mind, contemplating the punishment I was going to receive.

Then:

"Sorry Joy."

A shrug, a turn, a pat on the head of a certain victimised second year.

A stunned silence.

That was the first. I didn't associate it with the coin, of course. It was nothing special. A bully who decided to not be one anymore. It happens. He was bored. He wanted to see what it was like to be liked. To see a smile instead of a frown. A grin rather than a grimace.

It happens, doesn't it?

I think I put the coin in my pocket. I don't actually remember. It wasn't in my hand, at least. Later, I'd bought a chocolate bar from the tuck shop. Crunchies were my favourite, but I'd resigned myself to the cheaper Double Decker. The price difference was two pence. Thanks to my finding that coin in the hall, I had the required amount for my preferred choice.

My pockets were then empty of money.

But later, on my way home, passing the arguing couple, flipping the coin I shouldn't have had, the couple suddenly putting their arms around each other and laughing... I felt sick.

Not at the fact that a coin had mysteriously appeared in my pocket - I don't think I even noticed, as such. And not at the couple laughing and kissing where they'd been arguing and looking like one was going to slap the other.

No, I felt sick because something good had happened. I think. It was hard to pin down. I could feel a pull, in the pit of my stomach, towards the man and woman. As if my gut wanted to hug them.

It passed in a second, but I could still feel its echo for a long time after.

At home, I didn't eat much of my tea. I complained of 'women's problems' having not long started my periods, and went to bed.

I didn't sleep. I had dreams. They weren't nightmares exactly, but they did unsettle me. People smiling and laughing. Me in the middle of it all, huddled into a ball. Crying.

A shower, some toast and a giggle with Zoe on the way to school dragged me out of my subdued mood. By the time the first bell had gone, I was back to my old self.

And I'd left the coin on my bedside table, next to my alarm clock. It was about the only surface in my room that I kept clean. The clock, a simple digital affair with a huge (much used) snooze button held pride of place. I didn't want to accidentally hit anything else when I was woken, bleary eyed, by its insistent beeping.

So the coin was honoured to share that space, in a way. Plus, I didn't KNOW, but I had a funny feeling. It was a bizarre notion, but one I couldn't shake. I didn't want the coin with me. I wanted to leave it behind. I'd get rid of it later. Give it to my brother or something.

Morning register passed with the usual suspects making jokes or staring out of the window, wishing they were somewhere or someone else. The day itself bimbled along at a leisurely pace, not wanting to rush and be done with before it had had a chance to enjoy itself. By last period, I was walking in a daze, the insipid attitude of the day seeping into my bones to lull me into a zombie state. All that I lacked was a shuffling walk, arms outstretched, and a thirst for blood.

The only thing I did have a thirst for was orange Lucozade. Not for the sporty energy filled boost it might give, but for the taste. I liked it, and drank it by the gallon at home. I'd been given my pocket money the day before. It was hit and miss whether we'd even get it, let alone it be a regular Friday thing, so I was always pleased to receive the £5 I was allowed. I say allowed

- my brother could often be thrown a few coins, as if to a homeless tramp in the street. Even though I didn't get pocket money often, at least it was an amount that I could deem worth having.

That makes me sound selfish. I should have been pleased to have anything. I was, honestly. It was just that my friends would have money in their pockets all the time. I would have to make excuses and jokes to hide the fact that my parents were, in my friends' eyes, poor, but in reality forgetful and uncaring. So I was grateful, I really was. But peer pressure could be suffocating sometimes.

The corner shop was on my way home. It wasn't actually on a corner, but everyone called it that. It was a small newsagent that served the few surrounding streets. I'd thought about taking a job delivering papers but... well... I didn't. Laziness, perhaps, but again, the thought of comments from my friends - who would never be tied to a job when they can be watching TV or having fun (jobs were for adults) - was enough to never actually take up that particular form of employment.

Mr. Kirman was the owner. He was an old man, past retirement by a millennium. Though a schoolgirl such as myself thought anyone above the age of 21 or so was old, I realised Mr Kirman was far older than my parents and was quite probably a grandparent in his own right. He had a fuzz of grey hair that circled his head like a fluffy halo and wore a permanent smile that had etched crows' size nines in the edges of his eyes.

As I walked in, I could hear raised voices. A group of boys, Will Bronson's acquaintances (minus Will), were throwing a can of drink between themselves. Mr Kirman was asking them to stop their messing and either pay for the drink, put it back, or leave. They were laughing, calling him 'granddad' and tossing the can, every so often waving it in his face so he'd grab at it, then snatching it away again in a fit of laughter.

Mr. Kirman saw me and shook his head, telling me to turn around and leave. It was a kind gesture but one of the gang saw the signal and turned to me.

"Joy!" His name was Craig. I didn't know his surname but his nickname was Limb. He had a habit of telling his victims he'd tear them limb from limb and enjoyed the notoriety such a moniker gave him. My insides sank and felt like they wanted to crawl out of my toes toward the door.

"Craig," I said quietly.

"What are you buying me?" he asked, stepping forward. The other boys had stopped their game and were watching, their expressions those of hyenas circling a dying prey.

"Nothing. I just want a drink, that's all."

He imitated me in a stupid high-pitched voice I doubted he could make if his testicles had dropped. I just looked at him, not saying anything. Mr Kirman told them to leave me alone and get out, but they ignored him. So did I, for that matter. All I saw was the mighty Limb and his pack.

"Give me your money," he said, holding out his hand. "Your money or a kiss."

This made his brethren laugh. I didn't think any of them had touched lips with a girl, or touched anything else, either. Still, I didn't want to find out how far they'd go to experience it. I didn't get my pocket money often enough to have come to rely on it, so I decided to simply hand it over rather than risk a mauling or it being taken.

I reached into my coat pocket. My hands wrapped around the five pound note, and something else. I pulled them out. Laying on top of the note was a two pence piece. THE two pence piece.

I frowned. Craig snatched. The note and coin fell to the floor, the coin rolling to his feet. He bent to pick it up, leaving the fiver were it lay.

"Two pence? Who has five pounds and TWO PENCE? You been saving up, Joy? Charging tuppence a kiss?"

With a crooked smile I would happily have slapped off his face, he said: "Heads you go, tails you kiss."

I went to protest, but the coin was in the air before the first word was out of my mouth. I saw my hand reach out and grab it before it could land. Someone else must have pushed my arm because I certainly didn't catch it intentionally. Both my own eyes and those of my tormentor went wide.

Then my stomach pulled. Stronger this time, with a twist as if my intestines had suddenly knotted.

Then Craig spluttered.

Then he turned, took the can from the boy who was holding it and placed it carefully on the counter.

"Sorry, Mr. Kirman," he said. "I've changed my mind. I don't want this now."

Without waiting for a reply, he walked out of the shop with his entourage following.

Mr. Kirman stared, speechless. I bent to pick up my five pound note from the floor and ran before he could ask any questions. It wasn't that I didn't want to answer those questions, but saying anything about what had just happened would have made it something when it was nothing. It would have given it a substance and that would have meant it was real.

The Bully Brigade had turned right out of the newsagent. I turned left. It wasn't the way to my house - for that I would have had to have gone in the same direction as the boys - but I didn't care. I just need to be moving. A direction would have meant I was thinking and I SO didn't want to do that.

Another left turn and another brought be to Cambridge Road. It was a long street that had shops at one end and my school at the other. On the opposite side to the school were the Seven Hills. Rats the size of dogs were meant to roam free and only the brave dared to go in. Granted only a low fence, a horizontal metal bar held in place by knee high concrete posts, served to keep the unwary out and the beasts in, so I didn't exactly believe they existed.

But everyone said they did. So I had always chosen caution and had yet to venture inside.

Caution required thought, though, and I had left my thought on the counter next to the discarded can of drink.

I stepped over the bar and entered the domain of the Drat. Well, what would you call a creature that was part rat and part dog? A Rog? Talk sense.

I expected a chill to sweep over me, bristling the hairs on my arms even though they were hidden beneath the sleeves of my coat. It didn't happen. Neither was I attacked where I stood by other-worldly animals desperate for a piece of my leg or my throat. Nothing changed. Outside of the Hills was the same as inside.

I started to walk. I just needed to walk. I wanted the air to be crisp and the sounds to be muted. Neither was the truth. But I was, at least, alone.

Apart from the coin that should have been lying on my bedside table keeping my clock company but was now still held tightly in my palm.

Why would that make me feel like I was not alone? It was a piece of metal, not a person or a pet. It didn't have a voice or a soul. It was just two pence.

Sure it was.

I dropped the coin on the floor, not looking where it landed. I ignored its fall, letting it hit where it wanted. I was nonchalant. Uncaring. Otherwise occupied. And that took a lot of effort. My mind kept wanting to turn my head, to direct my focus to the dirt at my feet. I forced myself not to. I forced my feet to move and my eyes to remain fixed ahead. If I couldn't see it, then perhaps it could be left behind.

Perhaps it would leave me alone.

I didn't know what to expect in the Seven Hills. As such, my footing was unsteady and my sense of direction erratic. I almost felt like a ship in the Bermuda Triangle, my compass spinning out of control.

Get a grip, I told myself. It's a bit of wasteland. I looked back towards the road to get my bearings. As I walked further away, I calmed down. The cars and the people were ruffling my feathers and the solitude of the coinless Hills was smoothing them back down.

There was a steep dip, the surface treacherous with holes and dips and boulders. The ground beneath my feet shifted. My feet above the ground didn't.

I landed on my bum. It hurt. A small cloud of dust danced around me, laughing at my less than graceful decent. I coughed and it sounded flat as if the fullness of my voice had been squashed under my bottom by my fall. Something glinted in the setting sun, a flash that made me blink. I leaned forward and pulled the coin from the ground at my feet.

I almost said 'Hi.'

It was warm. I held it in my hands, letting the heat spread up my arms. I was suddenly cold and this was battling the chill into submission. I closed my eyes and let the desolation of the Hills wrap around me. For the first time in SO long, I didn't feel outcast.

Yes I had friends. Yes, Zoe and I were almost sisters, we were so close. But still. There was an edge - a boundary around me. A salt circle. I didn't know whether it was my own invention or that of others, but it was there. Mine, I suppose. People liked me, but I just couldn't give it all back.

In the Seven Hills, there was no-one to judge or to need or to bother. I felt at home, if a little dishevelled.

Odd that. I was in a place that most my age would avoid. Most any age for that matter. I'd not set foot in here in my life, yet I felt as if I knew it better than my own house.

I gripped the coin, the warmth dissipating into my body. Being there had altered my opinion of it. It was no longer something to cast aside. It was something to be held close.

I could have asked 'why me?' There'd be no answer. Who would I ask anyway? My parents? If I wanted the sort of derision that was usually reserved for my brother, then yes. A teacher? Hardly. As good as some of them were at teaching - and as dire as others were - I didn't think they'd quite understand.

What would I say?

<I think that, if I flip this coin, I can make people happy. Or I can make bad people good.>

A couple of incidents didn't make that the case. A coincidence or two hardly proved my gut feeling. I'd be laughed at. Talked about. I'd be taken to a counsellor. I'd be made to talk about how people seem to like me.

Narcissism, I think it's called. An exaggerated idea of one's own importance. I didn't have that. I had the reality of it. It was something I'd just lived with. People tended to do as I asked. I didn't often get told off or bullied or treated with anything but respect. In most cases, at least. Occasionally someone would slip through. But now, with this coin, it had been taken to a new level.

I needed to test it. I should make sure, before I said anything to anyone, just how true my feelings were or how effective the coin was.

And if I was right, if I could do it, then what?

I had an argument with myself. Part of me wanted to ignore the coin and do everything I could to get rid of it. Live the life I was living. Another part, stronger and more forceful, insisted that I should do something with this gift, or whatever it was. I should use it to help people. Yes, it made me feel sick. Yes, it scared me. But, I must have been given it for a reason, isn't that what they say in the movies?

For Spiderman, with great power came great responsibility.

For Joy, there came questions and fears and doubts.

Not that I had anything resembling power - great or otherwise. I had a poxy two pence coin, one that somehow wouldn't leave me alone. One that somehow acted like a magnifying glass to the 'liking me' thing. I just hoped that magnifying glass wouldn't, eventually, burn me out.

Well. If only you could turn your head and make HINDsight FOREsight. You can't, though. So I made my decision on a stupid, movie-inspired, sense of right.

In many ways, it was the right choice. For others. For those I aided and for those I indirectly helped by altering the outlook of the bully or the thief or the murderer.

It was also the path that led my descent into Hell.

If only I'd known. If I could have seen the future at that point, would I have carried on? I don't know. I really don't. As I stood, brushed off my clothes and walked out of the Seven Hills, I couldn't foretell that each flip of the coin would eventually feel like I was being flayed, the skin stripped from my body and the spirit stripped from my soul with every catch.

You know that the heels are going to kill your feet, but you still go on the night out in them, and suffer the pain. Not quite the same as knowing I'd suffer from helping people but doing it anyway, but I'm not the lyricist my brother is. I'm sure he wouldn't call himself lyrical. He'd say he was just weird, as if it was something to be proud of. Who'd want to be normal?

Well, I wouldn't mind.

I knew, though, upon leaving the Hills behind me and walking home, that I would keep that coin close. I'd do what I could, however it might make me feel. You don't have the voice of an angel and leave it to the frogs to sing. Or something like that. How come these things always sound better in my head? How come my brother could always twist the words around his little finger, having them dance across his tongue to whichever beat he chose?

There's been many times since then when I've wondered at my choice. After all, I'd only found the coin - or it had found me - the day before and already I was convinced that it was haunting me and making me do things. A possessed coin, perhaps, one with the spirit of... what...? A saint? Not something demonic, I was sure. Otherwise people would die when I flipped it. There and then, I'd chosen to keep it and let it guide me. To use it to help people.

I was always the decisive one, though. My brother could turn procrastination into an Olympic sport, if only he would get around to it. If this had happened to him, he'd no doubt be trying to rid himself of the tuppence for quite some time, denying the possibilities of the good he could do. I wasn't like that. It was happening and I had to deal with it.

On the way home, I passed an old couple. They had faces like walnuts, the lack of elasticity in their skin making it collapse upon itself. They must have been nearing the end of their eighth decade each and were holding hands the way I hoped I would be with someone when I was that old. The man was shuffling, leaning heavily on his stick and the woman was a little spritelier, with less of a shamble and more of an actual step as she moved. She laughed at something he said and the pair of them smiled warmly at me as I passed.

The coin curling through the air was welcome. The punch in my stomach wasn't, but I could live with that.

The old man stopped. I thought it was for a breath. He arched his back as if to ease his aching bones, then they continued to walk.

Except he was twirling his walking stick with a perfect Charlie Chaplin spin.

The pain in my tummy lasted longer that time. With each toss of the two pence, it worsened. But the smiles on the faces of those affected were a warm soothing hand to gently rub it away.

I revisited the Seven Hills many times after my first venture in. Whilst my parents thought I was drinking cider on street corners with my friends, I was exploring the dips and the hollows of the one place I felt calm. It was as if there was a lull in the world, particularly at the centre. No sounds from the busy roads that surrounded the wasteland could be heard. The depression prevented me from seeing the outside world, but also served to defeat anyone's attempts to seek me out. Not that anyone would. In all my time there, I'd not seen one other person enter.

That was fine with me. I liked the solitude. Just me, myself and the silence. And the coin. Even on the odd occasions I neglected to pick it up, it had always appeared in my pocket or purse. Once, when I had neither pocket nor purse, I'd found it under my watch on my wrist.

I gritted through the pain in my stomach. My parents, however, were uncharacteristically concerned. They became increasingly worried as time went on and I went from a grimace to a groan to a doubled up heap. I did my best to ignore it - it was the price of happiness - but they thought something was wrong rather than very right. Hence the hospital. Hence the tests for cancer or for Crohn's or for any other illness I might but didn't have.

The protests of a young girl were shouted over. Mum knows best. Dad couldn't bear to see his baby girl in so much pain. I wondered where my real parents were. I knew that, if this had been my brother, the same concern wouldn't have been displayed. Knowing that nothing would be found, I had no choice but to succumb to the invasions of the doctors.

School had been left behind and I was officially an adult, but the medical staff listened to my parents. I should have fought it. I should have hidden it. But how could I? I'd become some sort of avenging angel in the face of Sorrow, the flip of my coin being my sword and the catch my shield. And when the afflicted is my friend...

It had reached the point where I didn't have to see the person. I didn't even have to know them. I'd find the coin landing in my palm and it would feel like the number five bus was driving through my stomach. A couple find out they're having a baby naturally after numerous failed IVF treatments. A wheelchair bound ex-soldier would begin to feel his toes and eventually be able to move them. A car would manage to brake just before it hit the child. The failed engine on the plane would splutter into life once again.

It left me breathless and reeling on the floor, but it was ok. I'd chosen this. I'd accepted my fate so many years before. My parents and the doctors, of course, knew none of this. To them I wasn't fine. To them I was a stubborn girl who needed to listen to reason and let them help.

I was laying on my hospital bed. My mother was sitting beside me. She was reading a magazine, the fact that she was actually in attendance proof enough that she cared. She wasn't required to interact with me as well. I was pleased. She didn't need to be there. Nor did I.

I hadn't seen Zoe for a while. We were still relatively close, but she had a boyfriend. She had a life. My life was other people. I didn't own myself anymore.

I didn't even know she was pregnant.

But I felt it. I felt her anguish. Her pain. I felt the slowing of the baby's heartbeat as the placenta became detached.

I reached beneath my pillow and retrieved the coin. I hadn't time to pick it up from home when I was practically dragged in here, but I knew it would be there. My mother's attention was on whichever celebrity was being unfaithful to whichever celebrity with whichever celebrity.

She didn't see me toss it. She didn't see me catch it.

I woke up, groggy. My throat hurt. My stomach had a sharp, jagged pain across it. I was still in my hospital bed, but something was wrong. Very wrong. I had an empty feeling inside of me.

Shaun Allan

My mother was sitting next to me, not holding her magazine. My dad was standing next to her. When had he come in? My brother walked in a few seconds after, holding a cup of water. All three members of my family were there at the same time. That didn't even happen at tea time, really. It was darker, too. Later.

Once my mum had told me what had happened, I began to scream. And shout. And swear, something I didn't regularly do. They left soon after. It was the shock, of course. I'd get used to it. It was for the best. I calmed down a long time after that, though, even now, my anger bubbles up like Etna on the rampage.

I'd passed out. After a long screech of agony, I had fallen off my bed, clutching my stomach, hit my head and not got up again. They had rushed me to the operating theatre. I have no idea why seeing as they had no idea what, but they, in their infinite medical wisdom, had given me an emergency hysterectomy. Perhaps that explained why I had been hysterical upon finding that little fact out.

Perhaps it was because of what I'd done. What wrong I had righted. With the flip of my magic coin, I had reached out, taken hold of Zoe's umbilical cord, and reattached it. I'd held the unborn baby in my metaphysical hands until its - her - heartbeat had steadied and strengthened. She would be born four weeks later, fit and well with a good set of lungs and a beautiful smile.

I only know that because I... just, somehow knew it. I didn't see Zoe again. I couldn't. Not after the birth of her child had resulted in the loss of any chance at children I might have. I didn't blame her, not at all. Nor did I really blame my parents or the doctors. How were they to know? They did what they thought they should. What they felt they had to. Much as I had been doing.

I didn't deal with it very well. I almost felt as if I had actually lost a child, not just my womb. The spirits of any offspring I could have given birth too had been cut away to save me. Except I hadn't needed saving. I had been doing the saving.

My parents died while I waded through the mire of my misery. I couldn't stop it or help it, nor could I feel it. They were gone. They could quite easily have gone shopping.

The coin changed from being my friend and comforter to being my tormentor. I left home. My brother no longer lived there. He'd escaped, but I'd stayed behind. I wished I'd done as he had. I spent two days and two nights at the heart of the Seven Hills, without eating or drinking. I simply sat there. Wallowing probably, but at the time I needed what only the Hills could give me.

Focus.

I felt myself slipping away, and I couldn't hold on tightly enough. My sanity was a mist that was clearing in the morning sun and I was still walking around in the night.

I went home, showered and changed, then made myself comfortable at the computer. I needed to research. I needed help. I had lost my mind, I realised, long before - so I believed. At school. The day I found that coin.

Asylums. The internet can tell you anything about everything. I surfed using a mouse and keyboard to skim the waves of information. Eventually, I picked one at random.

Dr. Henry Connors. Psychiatrist. He was as good as any. Any port in a storm, isn't that the saying? Well, I was at sea and looking for somewhere to dock before I was dragged under by the Kraken of my craziness. Connors would suffice.

Of course, I was wrong.

I told him everything. From the coin to Will and the bullies and everything up to Zoe. I even showed him the two pence. He didn't laugh, as I thought he must. He just listened, then he gave me a hug and took me through to the recreation room of the asylum.

And I waved goodbye to the world.

I had hoped it would stop, the things I could do. Maybe taking away my womb would remove the power I had. My ability to become a mother had gone, so perhaps my ability to mother in the way I had been for so many years. It hadn't. As my own mother hadn't particularly known what she was doing, clearly I had no real awareness of such things either. The coin had gone. I suppose it couldn't enter the walls of the mental home, though I couldn't see why. But it was no longer in my possession. I can't remember when I'd lost it, but, as much as I was pleased it was no longer constantly by my side, I missed it.

But its absence made me realise something. When it all carried on, when I was still healing and fixing and suffering, I understood, finally. It wasn't the coin, not at all.

It was me.

Two years I stayed under Dr. Connors care. I don't remember all of it. Often I would be drugged to stop me screaming in a pain I couldn't possibly have. In that time, the asylum flourished. People seemed to want to throw money at Connors and he was glad to accept it. I didn't know, at first, if it had anything to do with me. It never occurred to me that it might. But then, one day, the drugs didn't work. Whether they'd messed up the dose or given me someone else's medication, I still don't know. Whichever is the truth is irrelevant. I was subdued, but not in the complete daze I would usually be in, oblivious to everything except my own name when it was called.

Connors took me to a treatment room. He showed me a photo. I don't recall who it was of, but the person, a man with a beaming smile of artificially whitened teeth, was obviously very wealthy. Connors told me to 'do it'. He pushed me to 'do my thing'. I didn't know what he meant at first. How stupid was I? Then I realised and did it.

Somehow.

Instead of flipping a coin and having my stomach wrenched from my body and shove back upside down, I pushed with my mind. It felt like I was licking the photo. Caressing the cheek of the millionaire's printed visage. 'Good girl' he told me. Then I was led me back to the recreation room.

I walked out of there the next day. No wonder the asylum was doing so well. No wonder it had doubled in size in the two years I had been resident. Connors had used me. He'd made me push people into donating, subsidising, approving. I hadn't known. How could I? The drugs masked it all.

Nobody prevented me from leaving. Why would they? How could they? A little push was all they needed. I was a fast learner. Always had been.

I returned to my parents' home. In the middle drawer in the kitchen had always been, for as long as I could remember, a writing pad and a pen. For all I knew, it had been the same one for all those years, never used apart from a quick shopping list or to jot down the odd phone number or two.

I wrote my brother a letter. I needed to explain to him. Whether he believed me or not didn't matter. He just needed to know. My parents would have thought it was all down to the hysterectomy and, to be honest, they could think what they liked. My brother was different - in more ways than one. He didn't suit this family. I was odd and our parents had been a couple who acted as if they didn't have children. Or that their children were there for the entertainment value. My brother was... normal. He had a dark, dry sense of humour and sometimes had strange, rambling thoughts, but he was just an ordinary guy.

He deserved to know the truth, even if he might think I was crazy.

I told him everything. Well, almost. Strangely, I could tell him about the coin and how it had affected me and what I could do, but I couldn't bring myself to talk about Connors and the asylum. I thought that, if I mentioned a mental home, he'd automatically dismiss everything I'd said. Besides, I didn't want to admit I'd been used. I didn't want to say that Connors had used my gift for himself. It made me feel dirty. It tainted all the good that I had done.

I told him what I was going to do. And how. And I said goodbye.

Beneath the writing pad was a pile of envelopes. All were stamped. Mum had a weird habit of getting a book of stamps and putting them on envelopes ready for when she needed them. She said she'd prefer that than having to write a letter and not having a stamp ready. It resulted in some messy envelopes as she made mistakes and scribbled them out - preferring scruffy to losing the cost of a stamp.

I wrote the address and slipped the envelope in, licking it carefully. I'd once read a story of someone who'd cut their tongue on an envelope and had baby cockroaches growing in the wound from where their eggs had been laid in the glue.

The post box was only a short walk away. I'd hoped the fresh air would blow the cobwebs away from my mind and clean out my soiled thoughts, but it didn't. Pushing the letter into the slot of the post box, I paused, looking at his name. It would be the last time I'd see him. Not that his name was him personally, but it was the closest I would ever again get.

Sin.

He didn't like his surname. Our surname. I didn't blame him.

Back at the house, I made myself a coffee. Sin and I had employed a cleaner to look after the place whenever we weren't there, but keeping the fridge stocked with fresh milk was something we'd neglected to ask her to do. Luckily, I took my coffee strong and black. Like my men, I used to joke back when I still knew what a joke was.

The cup steamed. It still remained untouched when it had cooled and the limescale in the water had floated up to form a film on top.

Time.

I walk upstairs. I'm not sure why I don't want to do this in the kitchen or in the living room. It seems more fitting to be upstairs in my own room. I hope that Olivia, our cleaner, won't be too distressed, but I can help with that. A little nudge now that will lay dormant until it's needed.

Do I lay on the bed? Sit on the floor? Stand in the middle with my arms out? It takes me a moment to wonder, worry almost - as if it actually matters. I sit on the bed. I may as well be comfortable, if only for a moment. I rest my arms on my legs and close my eyes.

A jump. I suppose that is really the only way. The only way to be sure. I wonder how people decide the method they'll use. Do they draw pieces of paper out of a hat? Stick them to a dart board and blindly throw? Perhaps I'm not that imaginative.

I can only think of one way. One that won't hurt others, that is.

My car is in the garage. It's barely been used for so long, I am worried that the handbrake might be seized. It isn't. The car, old but more reliable than any person I've ever met (and cheaper to run), starts first time. It beeps a hello to me, which is actually the warning alarm telling me there's not a lot of fuel. I have a 30 minute drive ahead of me. It will be enough to get me there.

I press the button for the stereo, wanting noise to distract me from my course but, after surfing through radio stations where the songs and ads claw through my ears like rabid dogs, I press it again. I enjoy the resultant silence.

My mind wanders, but that can't be helped. Parts of me want to turn the wheel, either to return me to the house or to force me across the central reservation and into oncoming traffic. I let them fight it out amongst themselves, but ignore their demands. I have my goal set.

The Humber Bridge. Once the longest single span suspension bridge in the world, apparently. Probably still one of the most expensive tolls, though. I know people who are afraid to cross it, fearful of it collapsing or a freak wind blowing them off into the River Humber. They'd rather drive the two hour round trip through Goole than the two minute crossing over the bridge.

It doesn't bother me. Even now, when all their fears are going to come crashing down upon me. I'm doing what I must.

I find it funny that, to park my car, I must cross to the other side, to the viewing area, and then walk back. There's an area on this side, but the walk to the bridge is further, and my legs might have more control over me than my hands, causing me to veer off my course. I have to pay the toll.

There used to be, before the bridge was built, a ferry that crossed the river. I suppose paying the toll is almost like paying the ferryman. Chris De Burgh would be pleased, especially with the pollution and colour of the Humber giving it a kinship to the Styx.

I park my car, locking it. Habit, of course, as it really doesn't matter if it's stolen. I won't be needing it. The walk to the bridge is longer than I expected. I pass a man on a bicycle and a couple. They're coming off the bridge rather than going on it. I'd rather not have them close to me. I don't want to upset them, or scar them.

Even now, I can't help myself.

I wait for a lull in the sparse traffic. I climb over the barrier, brushing the dirt, rust and flakes of paint from my palms. I may as well be clean as I do this.

It will hurt, I know. A lot. I may scream.

A random thought occurs to me. I should have an epitaph. A final word. Like the captain of the Titanic asking for more ice in his drink.

Name's Joy. I make people happy.

And it's killing me.

The world is going to have a good day. A happy day. A JOYous day, in fact. I suppose it's my leaving present. A pity I can't gift wrap it.

I feel something warm in my hand. I know what it is. I can't help but smile.

I put out my hand in a loose fist and slip my thumb under the two pence coin.

Flip.

And...

Catch.

###

About the Author

Shaun Allan is a bestselling, award winning author who writes multiple genres, including psychological horror, introspective and emotive poetry, young adult and children's. He has appeared on Sky TV to debate publishing, is a Wattpad Creator and Adim Founding Creator, and been commissioned to write companion stories for such movies as The Purge: Anarchy, The Boy, A Quiet Place, IT and Amazon Prime's Panic series. He also holds regular writing workshops at local schools. Many of his personal experiences are woven into the points of view and senses of humour of his characters, along with the places in and around his home town. His novel Sin has been adapted into a Chapters mobile game titled Straitjacket Lover and was optioned for television.

Shaun lives with his manic dog, Ripley (believe it or not). He works full time and, though his life feels as hyper as his dog, it probably isn't.

Honest.

You can read more from Shaun at:

www.shaunallan.co.uk

Facebook/Instagram/Threads/TikTok: @singularityspoint

X: @singularityspnt

Printed in Great Britain
by Amazon

51463655R00091